TEACHER RESOURCES FOR

RETOLD
WORLD
MYTHS

■

Reproducibles
and
Teacher Guide

Editor-in-Chief: Kathleen Myers
Managing Editor: Beth Obermiller
Senior Editor: Marsha James
Editor: Cecelia Munzenmaier
Book Designer: Dea Marks
Cover Illustration: Mark Bischel

WRITER
Rebecca Spears Schwartz
M.A. English
Educational Writer

© 1993 **Perfection Learning© Corporation**
1000 North Second Avenue, P.O. Box 500
Logan, Iowa 51546-0500
Tel: 1-800-831-4190 • Fax: 1-800-543-2745
Printed in the U.S.A.

6 7 8 9 10 11 PP 09 08 07 06 05 04

TABLE OF CONTENTS

continued

Welcome to the Retold Myths ■

Overview
of the Series

The *Retold Myths* series includes the following components.
- Anthologies of cultural myths
- Teacher Resource book with reproducible activity sheets for each anthology
- Classroom posters for each anthology

Reading Levels

The Anthologies

The *Retold Myths* are designed for use with students in grades 6-12 who are reading at or above the sixth-grade reading level. Illustrations, footnotes, highlighted vocabulary words, and cultural information aid students' understanding and enjoyment.

The Resource Books

The resource books which accompany the anthologies supply many reproducible activity sheets. The reproducible format allows teachers the freedom to use entire sets of activities or to select individual exercises.

   The activities are designed for students reading at or above the sixth-grade level. Lessons build on students' background and experience, providing links between the reader and the text.

Adapting the Classics:
A Rationale

The *Retold Myths* are based on the premise that all students deserve access to classic literature and that all students are capable of thinking at higher levels if their activities are managed properly.

   The *Retold Myths* introduce students who are reading below grade level to literature that is often the exclusive domain of the advanced and college bound. Through these adapted editions, students can become familiar with elements of great literature.

   Students who read the *Retold Myths* and complete the accompanying activities share in the body of knowledge which defines the culturally literate. They are given the opportunity to understand allusions to the rich heritage of literature. They experience diverse oral and written traditions. Most important, they will be guided to examine the best in themes and ideals recorded by human beings through the ages.

Retold Myths Teacher Resource Book:
Designed for Effective Teaching

Activities in this resource book are arranged in a logical progression to assist students' comprehension. The resource book is divided into sections for each story or section in the anthology. Each Teacher Resource section has a uniform set of prereading and postreading activities.

Prereading Activities

Two brief but effective activities will get students ready to read.

Spotlight on Vocabulary. This prereading activity highlights ten vocabulary words from the "Vocabulary Preview" accompanying each selection in the anthology. (These words also appear in **boldface type** in each work.) Students choose the appropriate word to complete each sentence. The words are used in context similar to that used in the story.

Setting the Stage. This second prereading activity provides the anticipatory set for reading the selection. Background and motivation are given in a short, stimulating activity designed to make students more attentive readers.

Postreading Activities

A rich array of postreading activities is offered. These activities will test recall and comprehension, enhance critical thinking skills, stimulate the imagination, and expose students to important literary skills. Postreading activities include the following.

It Happened Like This. The first postreading activity checks understanding of plot development. Recall of important facts and details is tested in a multiple-choice format.

Vocabulary Review. Students check their comprehension of the ten words featured in "Spotlight on Vocabulary." This time, words appear in sentences from the selection. The guided repetition of these words helps build certainty.

Literary Focus. These activities zero in on developing literary skills by examining plot, character, setting, and themes in a variety of imaginative ways.

The Reading-Writing Connection: Unlocking Passages. This postreading activity calls on students first to write their interpretation of a passage from the myths and then to make written inferences about it. To conclude the activity, students respond in personal journals to the passage.

Writing Corner. These writing activities invite students to personally respond to the entire myth. Students might be asked to invent new endings, further round out characters, express a point of view, write a letter, create a humorous tale, or write persuasively.

One Step Further. This section contains a number of suggestions for further extension of students' interest in the myths and their cultural traditions. Open-ended discussion questions in this activity invite students to interpret the entire reading section. Suggestions for extended activities include project and research topics and small-group activities.

Response Key

Answers to activities are given in the response key.

Name_____

SPOTLIGHT ON VOCABULARY

Study the words and meanings shown in the box.
Then complete each sentence below by writing the
correct word on the line.

appease—calm; lessen	**fertile**—able to produce life
brooding—thinking seriously	**former**—previous; earlier
contended—claimed; stated	**intact**—in one piece
drastic—extreme	**intrigued**—fascinated; charmed
eternity—endless time; life after death	**sorely**—painfully; unbearably

1. Will the new rules bring _____ change, or will we barely notice the difference?

2. After his dog died, the little boy missed his pet _____ .

3. The letter was late because it went to Sean's _____ address where he lived last year.

4. Lenay hoped that promising to learn her part by tomorrow would _____ the director's anger.

5. Ramon was so _____ by the chilling story that he didn't hear the doorbell.

6. The idea of _____ gives many people hope for a better life after death.

7. The timekeeper declared that Reynaldo had won the dash, but Li's coach _____ that Li had finished first.

8. After the accident, Raphael couldn't stop _____ over his carelessness.

9. The earthquake shattered our windows; none were left _____ .

10. The _____ soil produced giant tomatoes.

THE DEATH OF OSIRIS

SETTING THE STAGE

These questions will help you get ready to read "The Death of Osiris." Prepare to discuss the questions by jotting down answers on the lines.

1. The god Osiris is the rightful king of Egypt. But his brother Set plays a nasty trick to steal Osiris' throne.

   How might Set's theft of the throne affect each of these people?

   Osiris

   _____

   _____

   Isis, Osiris' wife

   _____

   _____

   Egyptian people

   _____

   _____

   Set

   _____

   _____

   Horus, son of Isis and Osiris

   _____

   _____

continued

RETOLD WORLD MYTHS
© 1993 Perfection Learning Corporation, Logan, Iowa 51546

2. Set thinks he is rid of Osiris. But he's in for a surprise. How might
    the following facts affect the way the story ends?

Fact	Predicted Ending
Isis has magical powers	
Isis and Osiris have a child	
Set is hated by the people of Egypt	
Set fails to destroy Osiris' body	

Share your answers with your classmates. Then compare your
predictions with what happens in the myth.

Name_____

IT HAPPENED LIKE THIS

Write the letter of the best answer on the line.

_____ 1. Set designs the golden casket to capture Osiris because Set
   a. wants to rule Osiris' kingdom.
   b. is tired of hearing Osiris boast.
   c. thinks Isis will marry him once Osiris is gone.

_____ 2. Set kills Osiris by
   a. poisoning his food.
   b. burying him in the desert.
   c. throwing the casket into the Nile.

_____ 3. Isis uses her magical powers to
   a. kill those who murdered Osiris.
   b. disguise herself as she searches for Osiris.
   c. create a monster to destroy Set.

_____ 4. The rulers of Byblos don't know that the tamarisk tree has
   a. perfume that will poison them.
   b. roots that will sprout many more trees.
   c. a trunk that holds Osiris' coffin.

_____ 5. Isis casts spells on the royal baby in Byblos because
   a. she wishes him to live forever.
   b. she wants him to replace Osiris.
   c. his parents asked her to make the baby stronger.

_____ 6. Once the king and queen discover who Isis is, they
   a. give her the tamarisk tomb.
   b. hold a festival in her honor.
   c. promise to help her fight Set.

_____ 7. Set chops up Osiris' body
   a. to hurt Isis.
   b. to destroy Osiris forever.
   c. so he can claim Osiris' treasures.

_____ 8. Isis collects the pieces of Osiris' body and
   a. builds a pyramid to bury them.
   b. restores Osiris to life.
   c. takes them to the Underworld.

_____ 9. Osiris decides to return to the Underworld because he
   a. misses the power he had there.
   b. believes Horus should become king.
   c. wishes to help the dead.

_____ 10. Osiris promises Isis all of the following *except*
   a. she will never grow old.
   b. each spring will remind her of him.
   c. he will help Horus overcome Set.

RETOLD WORLD MYTHS
© 1993 Perfection Learning Corporation, Logan, Iowa 51546

Name_____

VOCABULARY REVIEW

These sentences are taken from the story. Circle
the answer that comes closest in meaning to each
word in **dark type.**

1. "Osiris ruled the **fertile** land of Egypt with his wife Isis."

    a. endless   b. sandy   c. life-giving

2. "Every one of them would be happy to spend **eternity** in such a
    charming place."

    a. money   b. life after death   c. tomorrow

3. " 'I feel like I rule a pile of sand. All that's going to change,' Set
    contended, raising his voice."

    a. nodded   b. grumbled   c. claimed

4. "The young women were **intrigued** by this strange woman who
    looked like one of royal blood."

    a. fascinated   b. worried   c. threatened

5. "[The child] reminded [Isis] of her own young son Horus, whom
    she **sorely** missed."

    a. painfully   b. barely   c. once

6. "[Isis] saw how frightened the child's parents were. To **appease**
    their fear, she removed her disguise."

    a. increase   b. see   c. calm

7. "Egypt was beginning to look like the deserts of Set's **former**
    kingdom."

    a. distant   b. earlier   c. strange

8. " 'Egypt suffers under Set's rule. We'll have to do something
    more **drastic,**' Isis continued."

    a. clever   b. extreme   c. dishonest

9. "Set knew how important it was for the body to remain **intact**
    after death."

    a. in one piece   b. untouched   c. buried

10. "[Osiris] looked tired and he spent more and more time **brooding**
    by himself."

    a. sleeping   b. reading   c. thinking

THE DEATH OF OSIRIS

LITERARY FOCUS: CHARACTERISTICS OF MYTHS

We can understand ancient peoples by reading or hearing their myths. That's because myths reflect some of the most deeply held views of a culture.

Most myths include one or more of these characteristics, or traits:

- heroes of a culture
- religious beliefs—about creation, death, God or gods, and souls
- values—what is good or evil; what is worth striving for
- explanations of events in nature—why seasons change, why there is thunder
- supernatural elements—magical powers and spirits

Review "The Death of Osiris" to find evidence of these characteristics of myths.

1. Name the heroes on which this myth focuses.

_____

_____

continued

Egyptian gods

RETOLD WORLD MYTHS
© 1993 Perfection Learning Corporation, Logan, Iowa 51546

2. The chart below shows one example of four characteristics from "The Death of Osiris." Find two more examples of each characteristic from the myth. You may use a quote from the story or summarize an example in your own words.

Religious beliefs	Values
a. *The Egyptians "knew that earthly life was but a step toward the next." (page 5)*	a. *"The Egyptians took great delight in such a well-made casket." (page 5)*
b.	b.
c.	c.

Explanations of nature	Supernatural elements
a. *"This is how a tree became the tomb of the god of all growing things. Perhaps that is why the tamarisk quickly grew to be the largest of its kind." (page 8)*	a. *"Isis began her quest by changing herself into an elderly woman." (page 7)*
b.	b.
c.	c.

3. Which of the five characteristics of myths listed on page 10 seem most important in "The Death of Osiris"? For example, is the religious aspect of the myth most important? Or is this myth above all a tale of heroism? Or is some other characteristic most important?

   Form a small group with others and discuss your opinion. Also talk about how the story might change if other characteristics were more strongly emphasized.

Name_____

THE READING-WRITING CONNECTION:
UNLOCKING PASSAGES

Answer the questions about these passages taken from "The Death of Osiris." (Go back to the story if you need more clues.) Write your response to part *c* of each question on a separate sheet of paper.

1. " 'There!' [Set] said, when his business was completed. 'That will take care of Osiris—in this world and the next!' " (page 12)

   a. What does the passage mean as used in the story?

   _____

   _____

   b. Set is glad to have gotten rid of Osiris. But how might his brother's death affect Set's own future?

   _____

   _____

   _____

   _____

   c. **Journal writing:** Set is a god—yet, like humans, he is jealous. Describe a time when you saw a jealous person try to hurt another. What did that incident teach you about jealousy?

2. "But the most powerful medicine was Isis' love for her husband." (page 13)

   a. What does the passage mean as used in the story?

   _____

   _____

continued

RETOLD WORLD MYTHS
© 1993 *Perfection Learning Corporation,* Logan, Iowa 51546

b. How does Isis show her love for Osiris at this point in the story?

_____

_____

_____

_____

c. **Journal writing:** Describe how the power of love can heal or make things better in a person's life.

3. "After all, [Isis] was watching one of the world's great mysteries— the magic circle of life and death." (page 15)

a. What does the passage mean as used in the story?

_____

_____

b. Osiris is a "dying god"—one who is killed and comes back to life. Explain why the death and rebirth of Osiris might have been so important to the Egyptians.

_____

_____

_____

_____

c. **Journal writing:** Think of a "circle of life" you have seen: the change of seasons, birth and death, or grief and joy. Describe your feelings or emotions about this circle.

Name_____

WRITING CORNER: DRAMA

One way a story can come alive is through *drama*. Drama is a story brought to life by actors and actions on stage.

In modern times, classic stories are often revised to bring them to the stage or screen. To change a story into drama, a writer has to decide when to add or subtract dialogue (speaking parts) and action.

Also, drama scripts include descriptions of scenery and props as well as a character list that not only names the characters but also tells who they are.

Try your hand at creating a drama.

1. **The scene**
   First, select one of the following scenes from the myth to dramatize. You may also choose your favorite scene.

   ❏ Osiris gets into the casket at his homecoming party

   ❏ The rulers of Byblos discover Isis casting a spell on their baby

   ❏ Osiris comes back to life

   ❏ Osiris leaves Isis and Horus to live in the Underworld

   ❏ Other _____

2. **The character list**
   Now create your character list. Which characters will be in your drama? Name them and briefly describe them.

   Example: _Isis—queen of Egypt, wife of Osiris the king_

Character	Description
_____	_____
_____	_____
_____	_____
_____	_____

continued

RETOLD WORLD MYTHS
© 1993 Perfection Learning Corporation, Logan, Iowa 51546

3. **Scenery, costumes, and props**
   What scenery, costumes, and props will you use? An example of
   scenery would be a painted scene of the Nile. A costume might be
   a jeweled headdress or a pale yellow robe. An example of a prop
   would be a casket.

_____

Scenery

_____

Costumes

_____

Props

_____

4. **Dialogue and action**
   Now review the scene and jot down how you want to change, add,
   or cut dialogue. Insert descriptions of the action you want to take
   place. Finally, decide exactly when and how to end the scene.
   Write your dialogue on a separate sheet of paper.
       The following is an example of dialogue and action from a
   scene on page 7:

   (*It is the next morning, in the royal bedchamber. Isis, wearing a
   pale yellow robe, suddenly sits up in bed, eyes wide.*)

   Isis *(to herself):* Where's Osiris? Could he still be at the party?

   (*Isis' thoughts are interrupted by wild knocking at her door. A
   servant enters.*)

   Servant: Oh, Isis. I have some horrible news! The worst there
   could be! Set has killed Osiris!

continued

5. **The drama**
   Share your work with a classmate. Ask for suggestions to make
   your work better. Next, change your script where needed. Then
   write the final version of your drama. Be sure to include the list
   of characters, costumes, props and scenery before the dialogue and
   action.

   If possible, you might want to stage your drama for another class
   or for a special event.

RETOLD WORLD MYTHS
© 1993 Perfection Learning Corporation, Logan, Iowa 51546

THE DEATH OF OSIRIS

ONE STEP FURTHER

Class discussion

1. How would you describe Set? How is Osiris different from Set? What is the cause of their conflict? Why does Osiris allow himself to be tricked by Set?

2. Describe the relationship between Isis and Osiris. How important is Isis in saving Egypt from Set? Is this goddess good, evil, or a mixture of both? Explain your response.

3. In what ways are Isis, Osiris, and Set godlike? In what ways are they more like humans? Are they different than what you expect mythical gods to be? Why or why not?

4. The ancient Egyptians believed their rulers were gods. Do Americans expect their leaders to be better than they are? Do they expect superhuman things of them? Explain your responses.

5. The struggle between good and evil is an important part of this myth. Who or what represents good in the story? Who or what represents evil? At what point in the story is this struggle most serious? Does good or evil win? Explain.

Written or oral reports

1. This myth explains that Egyptians built large tombs so that dead people would be comfortable in the next life. The great Egyptian pyramids were actually built as burial vaults for their pharaohs. Pick one of the topics below to research. Then report the most interesting facts to your class. Use pictures or photos with your report, if possible.

a. Research how the pyramids were built and who built them. Learn why they were called one of the Seven Wonders of the Ancient World. Then report to your class on this topic.

b. Find out more about King Tutankhamen and the treasures found in his tomb. Why was the discovery of his tomb and its treasures so remarkable? What exactly was found in the tomb? What legends and rumors have been told about the tomb? Report your findings to the class.

2. Read "The Theft of Persephone."* What are the likenesses between this Greek myth and "The Death of Osiris"? How do the two myths differ? Write up your analysis in a short report. You might include a chart to show the major likenesses and differences.

3. Osiris tells Isis that "there is a time for death as well as life—even for gods." Compare this message with what other religions believe about death, rebirth, and the cycles of life. You might read from Ecclesiastes, chapter 3, verses 2-8 of the Bible. What is the overall message or theme of these verses? You could also research the Hindu and Buddhist mandala, or wheel of life. What do the major religions—Egyptian, Christian, Jewish, Buddhist, Hindu, and Muslim—teach about the circle or cycle of life? Write up your research and opinions.

4. Learn more about hieroglyphics, the ancient Egyptian system of writing. Explain why the Rosetta Stone is important. Find out why the ancient Egyptians included hieroglyphics in the tombs of their dead. For example, you might research the hieroglyphics found in the tomb of Hesire. Report your findings to the class.

5. Read some other Egyptian myths. Then present a review of these myths to your class. Include the one you like best and the one you like least. Also explain the reason for your opinions.

Creative writing activities

1. The legend of the tamarisk tree in this myth tells why the tree is so large. Write your own myth to explain something in nature—the height of a mountain, the hugeness of a Sequoia tree, or the origins of thunderstorms, for example.

*One version can be found in *Retold Classic Myths, Volume 2.*

continued

2. Write lyrics to a song that might be used to comfort Isis on her journey home from Byblos. Set the lyrics to music, if you wish.

3. Suppose you are the royal historian for ancient Egypt. Write your account of events at the homecoming party. Remember that your words will be the history that others will read centuries later.

4. Write a poem Osiris might compose for Isis to explain why he has to return to the Underworld.

5. Create a story in which a character knows a special word that gives him or her magical powers. Be sure to include a conflict which the character overcomes by using the word.

Artistic activities

1. Design an invitation to the homecoming party Set gave for Osiris.

2. Find out about hieroglyphics and the Rosetta Stone. Then make a clay tablet with hieroglyphics on it, or make a replica of part of the Rosetta Stone. Write a brief explanation of your object and display it with the object.

3. Find some pictures of an ancient Egyptian temple and construct a small-scale model of the temple. Write a brief explanation of what your model represents and give some background history. Then display the model with your explanation.

4. Make a map to show Isis' journeys in this myth. Include both of her searches for her husband's body. Remember, the first search leads her to Byblos and the second search takes her across Egypt. Base your map partly on a real map of Egypt and the Mediterranean lands.

5. Create a "family portrait" of Isis, Osiris, Horus, Set, and Nephthys.

Small-group activities

1. Pick your favorite scene from this myth and prepare a reading of it to be recorded on tape. Have one person be the narrator or storyteller. Choose other group members to play the parts of the characters. Plan to use background music and sound effects. Add more dialogue to the scene, if needed. Be sure the dialogue is true to the story. After you make your recording, play it to the class or some other group who would enjoy it.

2. Find out about the structure and government of ancient Egyptian society. Who was at the top of society, and who was at the bottom? What jobs did people have? What were the roles of women, men, and children? How was the society ruled? Divide up the research. Then prepare a panel report for the class. For your report, make a poster that will show the structure of society from top to bottom. Have another poster ready to show how the government worked.

RETOLD WORLD MYTHS
© 1993 Perfection Learning Corporation, Logan, Iowa 51546

Name _____

SPOTLIGHT ON VOCABULARY

Study the words and meanings shown in the box.
Then complete each sentence below by writing the
correct word on the line.

agile—nimble; quick	**features**—parts of the face
appetizing—tasty; flavorful	**felines**—cats
avenge—take revenge on behalf of someone	**ravine**—small, steep cut in the earth, usually made by running water
commotion—disturbance; uproar	**soundly**—completely
devised—designed; thought out	
emerged—came out	

1. Shannon asked me what color Bob's eyes were, but I couldn't clearly remember his _____ .

2. I knew that my pet cats were _____ , but I didn't realize that lions were too.

3. Raymond escaped the flood by climbing up the banks of the _____ .

4. The Eagles basketball team tried to _____ last year's loss against the Mustangs.

5. Rita is so _____ that she easily made the gymnastics team.

6. The pot of soup smelled wonderful and looked _____ .

7. The _____ the bear made looking for food woke the whole camp.

8. The new butterfly _____ from the cocoon.

9. Tomas slept so _____ that he didn't hear the alarm go off.

10. Marian _____ a plan to start her own gardening business.

Name_____

SETTING THE STAGE

These questions will help you get ready to read "The Twins' Visit to the Underworld." Prepare to discuss the questions by jotting down answers on the lines.

1. This myth revolves around a game similar to basketball. Imagine that you were challenged to a basketball match. Read the list below and decide which of these factors would most likely help you win. Rank your choices, with *1* being the factor that would most help you win.

   _____ Good teammates

   _____ Skill at playing the game

   _____ Desire to win

   _____ Fear of losing

   _____ Secret game plan

   _____ Confidence

   _____ Experience at playing the game

   _____ Calm under pressure

   _____ Good physical condition

   _____ Knowledge of the rules of the game

   _____ Bending the rules

   _____ Cleverness

2. In "The Twins' Visit to the Underworld," two humans dare to play ball against a team of gods.

   a. What kinds of advantages might the gods have?

   _____

   _____

   _____

continued

RETOLD WORLD MYTHS
© 1993 Perfection Learning Corporation, Logan, Iowa 51546

b. What might give the humans a chance to win?

_____

_____

_____

c. What might happen to humans who lost a game against the gods?

_____

_____

_____

As you read, notice what advantages the twins have and what advantages the gods have.

Mayan bat god

Name_____

IT HAPPENED LIKE THIS

Write the letter of the best answer on the line.

_____ 1. The twins play tlachtli with the lords of Xibalba to
   a. avenge the deaths of their father and uncle.
   b. become immortal.
   c. free the people in the underworld.

_____ 2. The lords put the twins in the House of Gloom because
   a. the twins will sleep well there.
   b. they believe the twins won't survive the night.
   c. the twins' father and uncle stayed there.

_____ 3. The twins get flowers for the lords
   a. from the gardens by the tlachtli court.
   b. by tricking the demons.
   c. with the help of the ants.

_____ 4. If the twins survive, they
   a. can restore life to their father and uncle.
   b. will become immortal.
   c. can return to earth to warn others.

_____ 5. A bat severs Hunahpú's head, but
   a. he can hear and speak through Ixbalanqué.
   b. Ixbalanqué promises to get it back.
   c. Ixbalanqué shapes a turtle into a head.

_____ 6. When the Xibalba chase the rabbit,
   a. Ixbalanqué snatches Hunahpú's head.
   b. Hunahpú's misshapen head turns into a human head.
   c. the turtle frees Hunahpú's head with magic.

_____ 7. The lords can't defeat the twins so they
   a. burn them to ashes in a bonfire.
   b. chase them from the underworld.
   c. hang their heads on a calabash tree.

_____ 8. The twins return to the underworld and
   a. begin turning the people against the lords.
   b. awe the lords with their magical fire.
   c. destroy the six houses.

_____ 9. The lords of Xibalba die in the twins' fire because
   a. the rabbit steals their fireproof robes.
   b. the fire is as hot as the sun.
   c. the twins don't resurrect them.

_____ 10. When the twins toss the two heads into the sky, the
   a. screams are heard around the world.
   b. stars burn brighter than ever before.
   c. sun and moon are created.

RETOLD WORLD MYTHS
© 1993 Perfection Learning Corporation, Logan, Iowa 51546

THE TWINS' VISIT TO THE UNDERWORLD

VOCABULARY REVIEW

These sentences are taken from the story. Circle the answer that comes closest in meaning to each word in **dark type.**

1. "Indeed the two made such a **commotion** that the earth shook beneath their feet."

    a. song   b. uproar   c. joke

2. " 'There's a strong chance that we're good enough to defeat the Xibalba,' [said Hunahpú]. 'It would also give us a chance to **avenge** the deaths of our father and uncle,' said Ixbalanqué."

    a. invite   b. study   c. take revenge

3. "[The twins] crossed a deep **ravine** with a boiling hot river steaming below."

    a. well   b. cave   c. cut in the earth

4. "Nevertheless, when morning came, Hunahpú and Ixbalanqué boldly marched out to the ball court. And they **soundly** defeated the lords of the underworld!"

    a. completely   b. loudly   c. kindly

5. "The fiends exchanged glances and slowly nodded. The twins really didn't look very **appetizing.**"

    a. handsome   b. tasty   c. heavy

6. "There they were surrounded by hungry **felines,** who growled and spit and clawed at them."

    a. bears   b. cats   c. monsters

7. "But the twins found some old bones and threw them to the beasts. The jungle cats were satisfied, and the twins **emerged** unhurt the next morning."

    a. met up   b. came out   c. rolled by

8. "Swift rabbit, strong-winged hawk, and **agile** goat—at least one of every kind of animal—gathered around the brothers."

    a. quick   b. cheerful   c. furry

9. " 'Brother,' said Ixbalanqué, 'sit still and I'll shape your **features.**' "

    a. hair   b. future   c. face

10. "The lords of Xibalba talked and argued for a long time. Finally they **devised** a plan."

    a. designed   b. demanded   c. delivered

Name_____

THE TWINS' VISIT TO THE UNDERWORLD

LITERARY FOCUS: CONFLICTS

Conflict occurs when two or more forces or characters oppose each other. If it weren't for conflict, most stories would be *very* dull. It is conflict that adds excitement and action—and moves a story along.

   Most of the conflicts in this myth involve the twins' outwitting or defeating characters who oppose them. But there are also conflicts involving forces of nature—heat and cold, for instance.

1. Identify the conflict that occurs at each point in the story. Then write how the conflict is solved. The first one is done for you.

a. Conflict in the House of Gloom: *Demons are sent to frighten the twins.*	**Solution:** *The twins decide not to light their torches, so the demons don't see them.*
b. Conflict in the House of Knives:	**Solution:**
c. Conflict in the House of Cold:	**Solution:**
d. Conflict in the House of Jaguars:	**Solution:**
e. Conflict in the House of Fire:	**Solution:**

continued

RETOLD WORLD MYTHS
© 1993 Perfection Learning Corporation, Logan, Iowa 51546

f. **Conflict in the House of Bats:**	Solution:
g. **Conflict after the twins win the last game:**	Solution:

2. Choose two of the conflicts. Write the letter of each conflict in the blank. Then write another possible solution to each and tell what the outcome would be.

a. **Conflict:** _____

Another solution:

_____

_____

Outcome:

_____

_____

b. **Conflict:** _____

Another solution:

_____

_____

Outcome:

_____

_____

Name_____

THE READING-WRITING CONNECTION: UNLOCKING PASSAGES

Answer the questions about these passages taken from "The Twins' Visit to the Underworld." (Go back to the story if you need more clues.) Write your response to part *c* of each question on a separate sheet of paper.

1. " 'We must survive this somehow,' Hunahpú said, his teeth chattering. 'Remember what our grandmother told us when we were small?'

    'Yes,' replied Ixbalanqué, shivering. 'There are six houses here in Xibalba. Anyone who can survive a night in each one becomes immortal.' " (pages 27-28)

    a. What does the passage mean as used in the story?

    _____

    _____

    b. Why are their grandmother's words important to the twins?

    _____

    _____

    _____

    _____

    c. **Journal writing:** Whose words do you remember when you need hope or guidance? What are some "words of wisdom" this person has given you?

2. " 'This looks like our last evening in Xibalba,' said Ixbalanqué. 'I can't see how we can possibly survive the night in a place like this.' " (page 28)

    a. What does the passage mean as used in the story?

    _____

    _____

continued

RETOLD WORLD MYTHS
© 1993 Perfection Learning Corporation, Logan, Iowa 51546

b. How do you think the twins' attitude affects the way they handle their situation?

_____

_____

_____

_____

c. **Journal writing:** The twins survive in the underworld by using their wits and skills. Describe a time when you used your wits or skills to solve a problem or get out of a tight spot.

3. "So the Xibalba asked the fishermen to perform the [fire] magic on them.
    "At first the fishermen refused.
    'Oh, no,' said Hunahpú shyly. . . .
    'We don't deserve to have fine lords like you honor us by taking part,' added Ixbalanqué." (page 33)

a. What does the passage mean as used in the story?

_____

_____

b. What effect does Ixbalanqué's statement have on the Xibalba? Why do you think it has this effect?

_____

_____

_____

_____

c. **Journal writing:** Describe a time when you flattered (praised) someone or were praised but the praise wasn't sincere. How did you feel about the flattery? What would you do now in the same situation?

WRITING CORNER: DILEMMAS

All through the myth, Hunahpú and Ixbalanqué face a *dilemma*. A dilemma is a situation in which a person must choose between two unpleasant choices.

In the underworld, the twins play tlachtli to win. Each time they win or tie, they must spend another night in one of the houses—where they face death. But if they lose a game, they also face death. The twins' choice is to play to win. They rightly figure that they can somehow survive the night in each house.

Now write your own dilemma. Think of the next adventure the twins will have. Create tension by including a dilemma as part of the conflict.

1. **The Next Adventure**
   Briefly describe the next adventure the twins will take part in. What will their goal be?

   _____

   _____

   _____

2. **The Conflict and Opponents**
   a. Now explain the main conflict, or opposition, the twins will face.

   _____

   _____

   _____

   b. Who or what will oppose them? Remember an opponent can be a character, a force of nature, or even fate (a fortune or curse). Describe the opponent(s).

   _____

   _____

continued

RETOLD WORLD MYTHS
© 1993 *Perfection Learning Corporation, Logan, Iowa 51546*

3. **The Dilemma**
   The dilemma should happen because of the conflict. Put the twins
   in a tight spot where they face two choices—each choice as
   undesirable or deadly as the other.

   a. Write the details of the dilemma. What two choices do the twins
   have?

   _____

   _____

   _____

   b. Which choice do the twins make? Why?

   _____

   _____

   _____

4. **The Outcome**
   How will your adventure end? What will be the outcome after the
   twins make their choice? Write the outcome.

   _____

   _____

   _____

5. **The Adventure**
   On a separate sheet of paper, write a draft of the adventure. Then
   read it aloud to a classmate.
       Keep a pencil handy. As you read, if you or your classmate
   notices gaps or if some part seems confusing, mark changes or
   additions to the story.
       Then write your adventure, making the changes needed. When
   you are pleased with your work, present it to the class.

ONE STEP FURTHER

Class discussion

1. Why do the lords of Xibalba challenge Hunahpú and Ixbalanqué to a game of tlachtli? What are the twins' reasons for accepting the challenge? Do you think the brothers make a good decision? Why or why not?

2. How do the lords of Xibalba treat Hunahpú and Ixbalanqué? What does this show about their sportsmanship?

3. Explain the role that animals play in this myth. Why do the animals help the twins instead of the Xibalba? Then think of some other myths or fairy tales that include helpful animals. Compare these animals and their roles to those in the Mayan myth.

4. In myths, heroism is often rewarded with immortality. In what ways do the twins show they are heroic? How does their heroism help make them immortal?

5. Suppose the twins represent the best virtues, or good qualities, of Mayan society. What virtues do they stand for? If the Xibalba symbolize the worst in Mayan society, what do they stand for?

Written or oral reports

1. Find out more about the Mayan culture. In what countries did the Maya live? What crops did they grow? What animals did they tame or use? What did they contribute to world knowledge? Use the information you find to make a report to the class. You might organize your report as a travel guide to help classmates get to know the Maya, country by country. Or you might use your report to get others interested in learning about the Maya. Use maps and drawings with your report, if you wish.

2. Study the Mayan gods—the good ones and the evil ones. Then make a chart to tell about each god and his or her position and powers. You might include drawings of each god on your chart.

3. Read the Insights for the myth. Then compare Mayan burial practices to the Egyptian practices. You might wish to read "The Death of Osiris" and its Insights section to help you. If you need other sources, check with your librarian. You might also want to compare Mayan pyramids with Egyptian pyramids since both cultures used them as burial vaults. Why do you think there are likenesses in the burial practices of these two groups of ancient peoples living on two different continents?

4. Read other Mayan myths. Choose your favorites and record them on tape to share with your classmates or other classes.

5. Where and what is Chichén Itzá? In what ways was it important to the Maya? Why is it important to us today? Research Chichén Itzá and present your findings to the class.

Creative writing activities

1. Write a ballad about the origin of the sun and moon. A *ballad* is a poem that tells a story. It sometimes has a refrain—that is, repeated phrases that appear regularly. Often a ballad is set to music.

2. Continue this myth. You might tell what the people in Xibalba do after they are banned from playing tlachtli. You might choose to have the lords of Xibalba come back to life. Or you might describe how the twins got married or grew old.

3. Create a game that the Maya might be able to play, using materials they would have had. Describe the rules of the game and its purpose. Give a brief explanation of how it is played.

4. On the way to the underworld, the twins cross the river of blood. What tales might the river have to tell? Write what the river might reveal of its past and what it has seen.

5. Write your own myth about how the sun and the moon were created.

RETOLD WORLD MYTHS
© 1993 Perfection Learning Corporation, Logan, Iowa 51546

Artistic activities

1. Find a picture of an ancient Mayan temple or pyramid and make a model of it out of clay or cardboard. Try to build your model to a scale, such as 1 inch = 50 feet. Your teacher can help you figure the best scale.

2. Make a comic strip of your favorite scene from the myth. Include four or five panels to show the dialogue, or talk, and action. You might wish to make your comic strip large enough to fill a sheet of poster board.

3. Find out what a Mayan calendar looked like and make a model of all or part of it. Display your calendar along with a brief note explaining how it was used.

4. Read the Insights to find out more about how tlachtli was played. Then draw a diagram of the playing field on poster board. Label the measurements, the parts of the field, and the hoops. You might also include two teams in your diagram. And don't forget to draw in and label the tlachtli ball.

5. Make a poster of a scene from the myth. You might choose from these scenes or pick any other:

- the twins' journey to the underworld
- Ixbalanqué seizing Hunahpú's real head
- the twins playing tlachtli against the Xibalba

Small-group activities

1. Choose one or more scenes from the myth to present as a Readers' Theater.

2. No one knows what rules the Maya used to play tlachtli. Based on the information in the Insights, try to invent some tlachtli rules. Decide how many players should be on the team and how to keep score. Also define legal plays, fouls, and penalties for fouls.

3. Organize a Mayan Festival at your school. Divide class members into small groups—to come up with games, displays, costumes, decorations, and scenery (like painted backdrops and mini-pyramids). If possible, one group may want to arrange to serve refreshments that would be typical of Mayan food. Some students may wish to act as guides, while others may want to lead games.

Once the duties are divided, set up a date and time for the event. Then advertise the event with posters, flyers, or announcements. If you wish, make tickets to sell or give away to your event.

Name_____

SPOTLIGHT ON VOCABULARY

Study the words and meanings shown in the box.
Then complete each sentence below by writing the
correct word on the line.

agonized—worried	**quarry**—object of a hunt or chase
allegiance—loyalty	**scowl**—frown; look of displeasure
donned—put on	**truce**—peace agreement
hearth—floor in front of a fireplace	**vaulted**—leapt; jumped over
integrity—decency; honor	**wavered**—gave way; showed doubt

1. The ghostly image _____ and then faded away.

2. The dogs followed the trail of their _____ —a wild rabbit.

3. It takes great _____ to deal fairly with your enemies.

4. Many citizens swear _____ to the country in which they were born.

5. In winter, the best place to get warm is by the _____ .

6. The war had gone on so long that many were surprised when the opposing leaders signed a _____ .

7. Shy Oscar _____ for days over how to ask Angeline for a date.

8. Chris easily _____ over the pommel horse to win the gymnastics meet.

9. I could tell from Maria's _____ that she wasn't in a good mood.

10. The dancers _____ their costumes before the show.

RETOLD WORLD MYTHS
© 1993 Perfection Learning Corporation, Logan, Iowa 51546

Name_____

SETTING THE STAGE

These questions will help you get ready to read
"Finn MacCool's Revenge." Prepare to discuss the
questions by jotting down answers on the lines.

1. In this myth, suspense builds as you wonder what will happen to
    the hero. *Suspense* is the worry or fear you have as you imagine
    what might happen next.
        Imagine yourself in the following scene. Then in each box
    below, write the emotions or feelings you would have in this
    suspenseful situation.

> **A storm rages in the gloomy night.**

> **Inside the house, a door creaks.**

> **Suddenly the lights go out.**

> **Outside, someone screams.**

> **Without warning, something catches your ankle.**

    Did your emotions grow stronger or weaker as you imagined
    yourself in each part of the scene? With your classmates, share
    what you imagined. How similar or different were your responses?

continued

2. In "Finn MacCool's Revenge," one character wants to help another character. But first he must overcome old feelings of anger and jealousy.

   a. What kinds of things make people jealous?

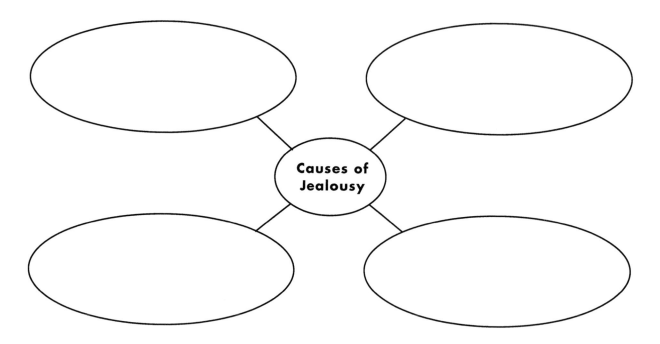

Causes of Jealousy

   b. If you were jealous of someone, would you try to overcome your feelings if this person needed your help? Explain your response.

   _____ Yes, if the person faced big trouble.

   _____ Yes, if the person didn't act is if he or she were better than I am.

   _____ No, because I couldn't truly wish to help that person.

   _____ No, because that person wouldn't accept my help.

   _____ Yes, because I might feel less jealous toward that person.

   _____ _____, because _____

RETOLD WORLD MYTHS
© 1993 PERFECTION LEARNING CORPORATION, Logan, Iowa 51546

Name_____

IT HAPPENED LIKE THIS

Write the letter of the best answer on the line.

_____ 1. Diarmuid promises to
   a. marry Grainne and help her escape.
   b. get Grainne safely away from Finn.
   c. help Grainne cast a spell on Finn.

_____ 2. Oisin advises Diarmuid to
   a. stay and tell Finn his plans.
   b. forget about Grainne.
   c. follow his heart.

_____ 3. Diarmuid decides to stay in the woods so that
   a. Angus can find them.
   b. Finn will look elsewhere.
   c. Diarmuid can face up to Finn.

_____ 4. The signal Oisin sends to Diarmuid is
   a. a flying spear.
   b. Finn's own dog.
   c. a stone from Cormac's castle.

_____ 5. Angus easily enters Diarmuid's fort by
   a. magic.
   b. the seventh door.
   c. a leap over the fence.

_____ 6. Angus whisks Grainne away, but Diarmuid
   a. escapes from the hut on his own.
   b. stays to sort out his feelings about Grainne.
   c. journeys north to talk to King Cormac.

_____ 7. Finn finally cools off, but Diarmuid and Grainne
   a. anger him again by having six sons.
   b. hire warriors for protection.
   c. still feel safer far away from Finn.

_____ 8. Diarmuid shouldn't hunt boars because
   a. boars are sacred to the Fionna.
   b. a boar seeks revenge against him.
   c. Grainne's spells are useless against boars.

_____ 9. Before Diarmuid kills the boar, the boar
   a. injures him severely.
   b. promises to haunt him.
   c. changes into the man murdered by his father.

_____ 10. Finn wants to help Diarmuid, but he
   a. forgets the healing spell.
   b. must heal himself first.
   c. struggles with himself too long.

Name_____

VOCABULARY REVIEW

These sentences are taken from the story. Circle the answer that comes closest in meaning to each word in **dark type.**

1. "[Finn's] eyebrows drew together toward the middle, giving his face a permanent **scowl.**"

      a. frown   b. crease   c. look

2. "All alone, [Diarmuid] paced the wall of the castle and **agonized** over his problem."

      a. growled   b. cried   c. worried

3. " 'Grainne has made me promise,' [Diarmuid] said as he ended his story. 'And such a vow is not to be taken lightly. But I have also sworn **allegiance** to Finn.' "

      a. power   b. time   c. loyalty

4. "Even the hounds snored as they slept on the **hearth** in front of the dying fire."

      a. floor by the fireplace   b. rug by the door   c. chair near the stove

5. " 'I doubt that Diarmuid would act with force,' " replied Cormac. 'You yourself know Diarmuid is a man of pure heart and great **integrity.**' "

      a. coolness   b. honor   c. leadership

6. "Diarmuid quickly **donned** his armor and took up his sword."

      a. cleaned up   b. put on   c. hammered on

7. "Grainne's eyes never **wavered** as she looked at Diarmuid's foster father."

      a. gave way   b. watered   c. saw

8. "With a mighty push, Diarmuid **vaulted** upward."

      a. looked   b. leaped   c. ran

9. "Finn and his warriors were astonished to see their **quarry** flying over their heads."

      a. best hound   b. hunted one   c. great weapon

10. "Soon all the wounded feelings seemed to be smoothed over. Angus did not feel completely secure with the **truce,** however."

      a. peace agreement   b. weak promise   c. dark secret

FINN MacCOOL'S REVENGE

LITERARY FOCUS: EXPOSITION

Story background—the information that sets the stage—is an important
key to understanding what happens in a story and why. This
background information is called *exposition*. The exposition usually
tells about the main characters, setting, and situations (the way things
are).

Answer the questions to see how the exposition of "Finn
MacCool's Revenge" helps prepare you for what happens. Page
numbers are given to help you find some information.

The Times

1. What kind of ruler governs Ireland? (page 42)

_____

_____

2. What positions do warriors have? (page 42)

_____

_____

3. How is Grainne's engagement typical for the times? (page 42)

_____

_____

Characters and Situations

4. Grainne

a. Traits: What is Grainne like? (pages 41-42)

_____

_____

continued

b. Situation: What is Grainne's situation? Whom is she engaged to marry? What are her feelings about this? (pages 41-42)

_____

_____

c. Effects: How do Grainne's traits lead her to change her situation? (pages 43-45)

_____

_____

5. Finn MacCool

a. Traits: What is Finn like? (page 42)

_____

_____

b. Situation: What is Finn's situation? How do Cormac and the warriors view him? What special power does he have? (page 42)

_____

_____

c. Effects: How does his age affect Finn's relationship with Grainne? How do Finn's traits affect the way he acts after Grainne elopes? (pages 42, 47, 57)

_____

_____

6. Diarmuid

a. Traits: What is Diarmuid like? (pages 43-44)

_____

_____

continued

RETOLD WORLD MYTHS
© 1993 **PERFECTION LEARNING** Corporation, Logan, Iowa 51546

b. Situation: What do Finn and the warriors think of Diarmuid at the beginning? To whom does he owe his loyalty? Where is he as the story opens? (pages 43-45)

_____

_____

c. Effects: How does sitting next to Grainne change Diarmuid's life? How do his loyalties conflict? (pages 45-46)

_____

_____

FINN MacCOOL'S REVENGE

THE READING-WRITING CONNECTION: UNLOCKING PASSAGES

Answer the questions about these passages taken from "Finn MacCool's Revenge." (Go back to the story if you need more clues.) Write your response to part *c* of each question on a separate sheet of paper.

1. " 'Then follow your heart. However, you must beware of Finn for the rest of your life,' Oisin warned." (page 45)

   a. What does the passage mean as used in the story?

   _____

   _____

   b. How might Diarmuid's life have been different if he had not followed his heart?

   _____

   _____

   _____

   _____

   c. **Journal writing:** Is it better to follow your heart (emotions) or your head (intellect) when making important decisions about your life? Explain.

2. " 'Father, I must stay here. I don't want to spend the rest of my life fleeing Finn,' [said Diarmuid]." (page 50)

   a. What does the passage mean as used in the story?

   _____

   _____

continued

RETOLD WORLD MYTHS
© 1993 *Perfection Learning Corporation, Logan, Iowa 51546*

b. Is Diarmuid acting honorably or foolishly? Explain your opinion.

_____

_____

_____

_____

c. **Journal writing:** Describe a time when you or someone you know decided to face a problem rather than run from it. Did the problem get solved? Why or why not?

3. "He turned to carry the life-saving liquid to Diarmuid. But then Finn thought of Grainne, and his hands began to shake." (page 57)

a. What does the passage mean as used in the story?

_____

_____

b. Did Finn refuse to help Diarmuid because he wanted revenge? Or was he trapped by his own emotions? Give a reason for your opinion.

_____

_____

_____

_____

c. **Journal writing:** What emotions build walls between people and what emotions can tear down the walls? What might stop these walls from being built in the first place?

Name_____

WRITING CORNER: FORETELLING THE FUTURE

The way Diarmuid is to die was decided before he was even born. It was foretold that he would be killed by a boar. Diarmuid's death is fated because his father killed an innocent man.

A. Suppose you are a fortune-teller and can see into the past and the future. Predict the futures of Grainne, Finn, and King Cormac. Imagine what events might have happened in the past—before the story began—that will influence these characters' futures.

The Fortunes

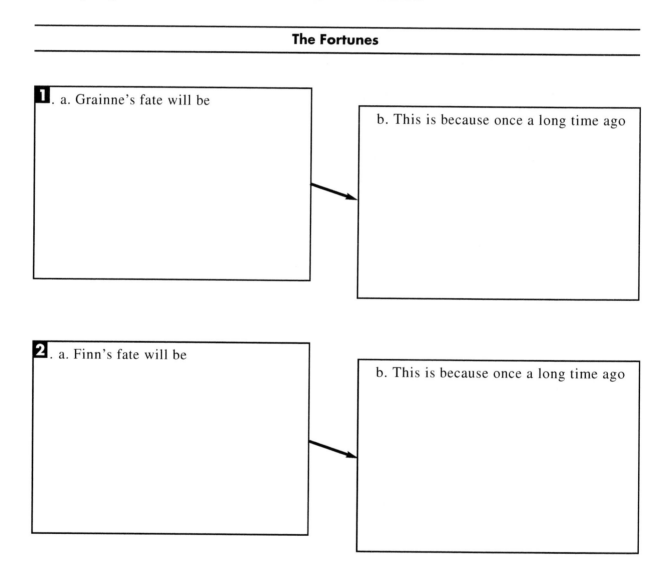

1. a. Grainne's fate will be

b. This is because once a long time ago

2. a. Finn's fate will be

b. This is because once a long time ago

continued

RETOLD WORLD MYTHS
© 1993 Perfection Learning Corporation, Logan, Iowa 51546

Name_____

FINN MacCOOL'S REVENGE

3. a. King Cormac's fate will be

b. This is because once a long time ago

B. Now tell one of the characters what his or her fate will be. Choose
    one of the fortunes. Then write a prediction based on that fortune.
        Predictions often use poetic language. For example, you could
    foretell a person's "path" through life. You might describe the path
    as "dark," "twisting," "smooth," etc. You could also talk about
    Fate as if it were a person. Try to make your prediction believable
    by using poetic language.

_____, you are a person who _____

_____

Your fate will be_____

_____

_____

_____

_____

_____

Share your fortune-telling with your classmates.

ONE STEP FURTHER

Class discussion

1. Grainne is "a very willful princess who was used to getting her way." Which other characters in the myth are used to getting their own way? Is willfulness a good or bad quality in these characters? Explain your response.

2. Several characters have magical powers. What are Grainne's magical powers? What is Angus able to do with his powers? Describe Finn's special power. How and when does each character use magic? Does any character seem to use magic more wisely or unwisely than the others? Explain.

3. Describe the traits that would make a perfect friend. How many of those traits does Oisin have?

4. Who is more heroic, Diarmuid or Finn? Give at least three reasons for your opinion.

5. Diarmuid is not able to overcome his fate, even though people with the power to help are close by. Do you believe in fate? Explain your opinion. How much does a person control his or her own life and future?

Written or oral reports

1. Read other folktales or myths from Ireland. (Your librarian can help you find these.) Choose two or three short ones or one longer one to read to the class. Practice reading aloud; then present your story or stories to the class.

2. Find out what feudalism is. How does the myth of Finn MacCool reflect the old Irish social and economic system? Report your findings to the class.

3. Grainne is one of many women who play an important role in Irish myths. Find out about another mythical Irish heroine. You might choose Maeve, Étain, or Dierdre. Share a story about one of these women with the class. You might include ways in which this heroine is like Grainne. Also, give your opinion about why the Irish consider her a heroine.

4. The myths of Ireland are part of the Celtic tradition. Many Celtic myths refer to a voyage to the Otherworld. Find out how the Celts described the Otherworld. Where was it located? How was it reached? You might also compare the Celtic Otherworld to the underworld of the Greeks, the Egyptians, the Chinese, or the Maya.

5. Where is Ireland located? And why is it called the Emerald Isle?

6. From the myth and its Insights, we learn that Tara is a well-known place in Ireland. Locate Tara on a map of Ireland. Find out about several more interesting places to visit in Ireland. Then find or make pictures of these places. Finally, present a travelogue in which you take others on a tour of Ireland through words and pictures.

Creative writing activities

1. Imagine that Diarmuid writes Grainne from the Otherworld. What might he tell her about his life there? Read the Insights to get some ideas. Then write a letter from Diarmuid to Grainne.

2. Suppose Grainne had not used magic on Diarmuid. How do you think the story would change? Revise the story to show those changes.

3. In the myth, the way Finn, Grainne, and Diarmuid look is described. But no physical details are given for Angus or Oisin. Choose either character and write a physical description of him.

4. Imagine that you attended Diarmuid's funeral. Write a diary entry that tells what you saw and experienced that day.

5. Write a poem or song about Grainne and Diarmuid's love. Or write a poem or song about Finn's lost love.

continued

RETOLD WORLD MYTHS
© 1993 Perfection Learning Corporation, Logan, Iowa 51546

Artistic activities

1. Make a collage that shows the thoughts or feelings of one of the characters. For example, you might picture Diarmuid's conflict between loyalty to Finn and his promise to Grainne. You could also show Grainne's feelings for Finn and for Diarmuid.

2. Choose music that might have been played at Finn MacCool's banquet. Then with classmates, create a dance to go with the music. Practice your dance; then perform it for classmates.

3. Create a family portrait of Grainne, Diarmuid, and their four sons. You might draw their castle for the background of the portrait.

4. Draw Grainne as a young maid at the banquet. Then draw her as she might have appeared years later at the feast attended by her father and Finn.

5. The early Irish used pins called *brooches* to fasten their cloaks. Design one of these pins for a character in the myth. The brooch should reflect something unique about that character. For example, you might use a boar for Diarmuid.

6. Study some samples of early Irish art. Then draw a scene from the myth using a similar style.

Small-group activities

1. Pick your favorite scene from this myth and prepare a reading of it to be recorded on tape. Have one person be the narrator or storyteller. Choose other group members to play the parts of the characters. Plan to use background music and sound effects. Add more dialogue to the scene, if needed. Be sure the dialogue is true to the story. After you make your recording, play it to the class or some other group who would enjoy it.

2. Find historically accurate recordings of old Irish music. You might choose music that was played at a banquet, wedding, or funeral. Also, research what instruments were used to make this music. Your librarian can help you find recordings and information. Have someone in the group find pictures or make drawings of the instruments. Present several recordings to the class. Have group members take turns presenting the music, explaining its purpose, and telling what instruments were used.

3. Read stories about several Irish heroes. Then make a chart listing elements which these stories have in common. Common elements might include subjects, like kingship or voyages. You might also find repeated references to fairies or the Otherworld. Also, consider ways in which the heroes are alike.

4. The myths of Ireland were old long before they were written down. Try an experiment to re-create the way the Irish people handed down their ancient stories. First, choose a short episode from a story. This might be a myth or an actual event, but it should be something most people in your class don't already know. Next tell several students the story. Then ask them to tell it to someone else. After everyone in your class has heard the story, ask students to write it down. Compare the different versions. Tell your class how many different versions you found. Also, try to explain why some parts of the story changed and others didn't.

5. Create a ballad or saga based on an Irish hero. You might collaborate on this project. For example, one person could write the beginning. Another could create the conflict. And someone else could resolve the conflict. Present your final work to the class.

IZANAMI AND IZANAGI

SPOTLIGHT ON VOCABULARY

Study the words and meanings shown in the box.
Then complete each sentence below by writing the
correct word on the line.

ceremony—service; ritual	**pillar**—column, usually used as a support
intruder—invader	**presence**—existence; nearness
molded—formed	**revive**—bring back to life
pathetic—poor; worthless	**searing**—burning; scorching
perish—die; pass away	**surveyed**—looked over

1. The hunter _____ the woods, looking for deer.

2. The paramedics used CPR to _____ the man hit by lightning.

3. The builder planned to use a central _____ to support the roof.

4. Most flowers will _____ in the hot sun if they aren't given enough water.

5. At the wedding _____ , the bride and groom exchanged rings.

6. The team _____ a sand sculpture that won first prize.

7. Most legal papers must be signed in the _____ of a witness.

8. The fire fighters battled thick smoke and _____ heat.

9. "You're too weak and _____ to win this fight," snarled the bully.

10. While we were away, a(n) _____ entered our house and stole our TV.

RETOLD WORLD MYTHS
© 1993 Perfection Learning Corporation, Logan, Iowa 51546

Name_____

SETTING THE STAGE

These questions will help you get ready to read
"Izanami and Izanagi." Prepare to discuss the
questions by jotting down answers on the lines.

1. In this creation myth, the gods Izanami and Izanagi have children
    who become the sun, moon, and islands. They also create gods to
    watch over mountains, trees, waterfalls, and all other parts of
    nature. Suppose every element of nature were watched over by a
    different god, or deity.

    a. Think of a waterfall—one that you have seen or one you
    imagine. Suppose that the waterfall is being watched over by a god
    or goddess. Explain what kind of personality this deity might have.

    _____

    _____

    b. Now think of a mountain. Imagine it is being cared for by a god
    or goddess. What might this deity be like?

    _____

    _____

    c. If everyone believed nature was filled with gods, what do you
    think people's attitude toward nature would be?

    _____

    _____

continued

2. In one scene from the myth, Izanami and Izanagi run into trouble
    because they do not follow a tradition, or custom. A tradition
    might be having a special holiday meal with your family or
    lighting a bonfire before the Homecoming dance.

    On the chart, list three traditions in your home, school, or
    community. Then write what might happen if someone ignored or
    tried to change the tradition.

Tradition	Consequences if not followed
a.	a.
b.	b.
c.	c.

As you read, notice what happens because a tradition is broken.

RETOLD WORLD MYTHS
© 1993 Perfection Learning Corporation, Logan, Iowa 51546

Name_____

IT HAPPENED LIKE THIS

Write the letter of the best answer on the line.

_____ 1. Izanami and Izanagi make land by
    a. throwing seeds from heaven.
    b. changing water into land with a jeweled spear.
    c. shedding tears which become islands.

_____ 2. Izanami bears a slimy leech child because she
    a. spoke first during her marriage ceremony.
    b. insulted other gods.
    c. called her brother a leech.

_____ 3. Izanami and Izanagi have island children only after
    a. making sacrifices to the gods in heaven.
    b. tearing down their palace.
    c. having a traditional marriage ceremony.

_____ 4. Izanami and Izanagi are happy about all of the following events *except*
    a. the creation of the first people.
    b. the birth of Amaterasu.
    c. the birth of the god of fire.

_____ 5. The death of Izanami is the first
    a. time that Izanagi cries for his wife.
    b. death in the world.
    c. chance Izanami has to return to heaven.

_____ 6. Izanagi can't rescue his wife from Yomi because
    a. monsters have taken over Izanami's mind.
    b. the dead want to stay in Yomi.
    c. Izanami has eaten food from Yomi.

_____ 7. Izanagi looks at his wife and this
    a. angers Izanami, whose body is decaying.
    b. blinds Izanagi, whose eyes are weak.
    c. sickens the monsters, who hate humans.

_____ 8. Izanagi escapes from Yomi by doing all of the following *except*
    a. throwing down his comb.
    b. starting fires all along the passage.
    c. pulling off his headdress.

_____ 9. Izanami vows to
    a. kill all the people of the islands.
    b. never let Izanagi sleep again.
    c. haunt the Japanese people forever.

_____ 10. From their conflict comes the couple's best creation, which is
    a. the blessed peace that follows a conflict.
    b. a rebuilt rainbow bridge to heaven.
    c. birth and death.

VOCABULARY REVIEW

These sentences are taken from the story. Circle the answer that comes closest in meaning to each word in **dark type.**

1. "They used the lovely jeweled spear as the central **pillar.**"

    a. signal   b. decoration   c. column

2. "When the palace was completed, Izanagi and Izanami stood in the doorway and **surveyed** their new home."

    a. looked over   b. thought about   c. cried for

3. "How could a god and goddess have given birth to such a **pathetic** baby?"

    a. poor   b. small   c. different

4. " 'The older gods believe it's unlucky for the woman to speak first during the marriage **ceremony,**' said Izanagi."

    a. tea   b. ritual   c. report

5. "Then the couple **molded** the first people."

    a. hardened   b. limited   c. formed

6. "But it was Izanami's last child—the god of fire—who caused the greatest grief. This god came into the world already **searing** hot."

    a. scorching   b. strangely   c. always

7. "His wife's death was the first in the world. After several unsuccessful attempts to **revive** his wife, Izanagi grew furious."

    a. look at   b. pray for   c. bring back

8. "Finally [Izanagi] sensed Izanami's **presence** in the surrounding darkness."

    a. coldness   b. craziness   c. nearness

9. " 'Destroy the **intruder!**' hissed one of the terrible women."

    a. reminder   b. invader   c. leader

10. " 'I now order a thousand a day to be born—plus half a thousand more. I will not let the people of our islands **perish.**' "

    a. grow old   b. move out   c. pass away

IZANAMI
AND IZANAGI

LITERARY FOCUS: IMAGES

This myth is filled with descriptions that help you imagine the scenery and characters. Here is just one example:

> The young god and goddess went and fetched a jeweled spear. They carried it onto the rainbow and poked it deep into the water. When they pulled it out, salty water dripped from the end of the spear.

This paragraph features several images. *Images* are descriptions that appeal to your senses of sight, smell, taste, touch (feeling), and hearing. These images can help you actually experience a story.

___

Sensory Images

For each passage given, write the image(s) that appeal to the sense(s) listed. The first one is done for you.

1. "As the years went by, Izanami gave birth to eight children—each one healthy and strong. And each of the children turned into a beautiful island. Soon trees and sweet-smelling flowers grew on the new islands. Waterfalls tumbled down the sides of mountains."

   List the image(s) that appeal to your sense of sight:

   eight strong, healthy children who turn into beautiful islands; growth of trees and flowers;

   waterfalls tumbling down mountains

   List the image(s) that appeal to your sense of smell:

   _____

   _____

2. "But it was Izanami's last child—the god of fire—who caused the greatest grief. This god came into the world already searing hot. As a result, Izanami was badly burned while giving birth to him. Indeed, Izanami became so ill with fever that she couldn't move."

   List the image(s) that appeal to your sense of touch (feeling):

   _____

   _____

continued

3. "The goddess wandered through the darkness, feeling more and more hungry. How long could she wait before breaking down and eating?"

   List the image(s) that appeal to your sense of touch (feeling):

   _____

   _____

4. "All alone, [Izanagi] paced through the beautiful palace and about the island where he and Izanami had once lived in such happiness. The waterfalls, streams, and trees all sang to him."

   List the image(s) that appeal to your sense of sight:

   _____

   _____

   List the image(s) that appeal to your sense of sound:

   _____

   _____

5. "Each day, there was less light to see by. It got so dark that he had to feel his way carefully with each foot to be sure he was still on the path. Finally he sensed Izanami's presence in the surrounding darkness."

   List the image(s) that appeal to your sense of touch (feeling):

   _____

   _____

6. " 'Izanagi,' a voice whispered. Izanagi knew it was his wife's voice. But she didn't sound happy. The whisper shaped itself into a long, sad sigh."

   List the image(s) that appeal to your sense of sound:

   _____

   _____

continued

RETOLD WORLD MYTHS
© 1993 Perfection Learning Corporation, Logan, Iowa 51546

7. "In the sudden glare he saw how Izanami's body had already
    started to decay. Her rotting flesh was falling away from her
    bones. Maggots were crawling all over her, feeding on what was
    left of her body."

    List the image(s) that appeal to your sense of sight:

    _____

    _____

8. "As he staggered along the darkened path, Izanagi heard the
    horrible creatures hissing and scurrying behind him."

    List the image(s) that appeal to your sense of sound:

    _____

    _____

Literal and Figurative Images
Some images can be *figurative*—the actual meaning of words is given
a new twist. For example, "the islands sparkled like jewels in the
ocean." The new twist is the comparison between the islands and
jewels.
     But most images in this myth are *literal*—the words have only
their actual meaning. This is true in the first example given.

9. Find the one figurative image in the eight passages given.

    _____

    _____

10. Explain how it is different from the other literal images.

    _____

    _____

    _____

    _____

    Discuss your responses with your classmates.

**THE READING-WRITING CONNECTION:
UNLOCKING PASSAGES**

Answer the questions about these passages taken from "Izanami and Izanagi." (Go back to the story if you need more clues.) Write your response to part *c* of each question on a separate sheet of paper.

1. " 'Why should Izanami die when I can't even harm the fire god?' cried Izanagi with despair. 'It isn't fair!'
      "But fair or not, Izanagi realized it was no use striking out against his children." (page 69)

   a. What does the passage mean as used in the story?

   _____

   _____

   b. Izanagi lets the three fire gods go into the world. Do you think this was the right decision? Why or why not?

   _____

   _____

   _____

   _____

   c. **Journal writing:** Izanagi learns that he can't change his children's true natures. If a parent and child have a personality clash, how should the parent deal with the conflict? Write your opinion.

2. " 'You must neither touch me nor set eyes on me,' [Izanami warned Izanagi.] 'You must return immediately to the land of the living.' " (page 71)

   a. What does the passage mean as used in the story?

   _____

   _____

continued

RETOLD WORLD MYTHS
© 1993 Perfection Learning Corporation, Logan, Iowa 51546

b. How does Izanagi react to Izanami's warning? How would you react in his place?

_____

_____

_____

_____

c. **Journal writing:** Describe a time when you asked someone to respect your wish for privacy or someone asked you to respect his or her privacy. How did you feel about the request? Do you think someone's request to be left alone should always be respected? Explain.

3. "[Izanagi and Izanami] had brought death and birth to their beloved island people. This was their final and most wonderful creation." (page 73)

a. What does the passage mean as used in the story?

_____

_____

b. In what ways was this final creation the most wonderful? Explain.

_____

_____

_____

_____

c. **Journal writing:** Imagine what the world might be like if there were no birth or death and people did not age. Briefly describe what would be the good and bad points of this situation.

IZANAMI AND IZANAGI

WRITING CORNER: SCRAPBOOK MEMORIES

Imagine you are Izanagi and you have kept a scrapbook of your life with Izanami and the children. This scrapbook *narrates,* or tells the story of your life. Fill in the pages of the scrapbook as Izanagi might have as his life unfolded. You will need to make up some of the details, but be sure your narrative is true to the myth. If you wish, draw in "photos" or other souvenirs of the past.

1. **Wedding Bells** Thoughts about marriage to Izanami:	3. **Memories of the Children** Happy and sad moments with the children. Some of their accomplishments too:
2. **Wedding Bells Again** Hopes after second marriage ceremony:	

continued

4. **Izanami's Death**
   Emotions about her death:

5. **Our Worst Conflict and How We Solved It**
   Thoughts about the conflict with Izanami after her death:

6. **Fondest Memories**
   The best of our life together:

ONE STEP FURTHER

Class discussion

1. "Izanami and Izanagi" is a creation myth. What questions does it answer about how things began? Which of these questions might be asked by people all over the world? Which questions might be unique to Japan? Can you see any similarities between this myth and other creation stories you know? Explain your answer.

2. What does this tale teach about traditions? Do you agree with this lesson? Explain your opinions.

3. The sun, Amaterasu, is a goddess, not a god. Many other cultures considered the sun male and the moon female. Why do you think the sun god is usually male in the tales from other cultures? What ideas might the ancient Japanese have had about the role of females?

4. The character to first experience death is Izanami—a deity. Why didn't the gods just give death to humans instead of having one of their own die? In this myth, what other things or situations must the gods deal with before humans experience them?

5. Describe Yomi, the Japanese underworld. What elements of Yomi are as you would expect in an underworld? What is surprising about Yomi? How does Yomi compare to other underworlds you may have read about?

Written or oral reports

1. Read more about Japanese wedding ceremonies. How do these compare to the ritual described in the myth? How do these compare to wedding ceremonies you are familiar with? Where do Japanese weddings usually take place? What vows are said? Is music used? Is there a reception or dance afterward? Report to your class on Japanese weddings. If possible, find or draw photos of a typical Japanese wedding to use with your report.

2. Find and read other tales about the Japanese sun goddess and moon god. Also, find tales of the Greek sun god and moon goddess. How are the Japanese and Greek moon deities similar? How do they differ? Prepare a chart to show the likenesses and differences. Then tell the class a little about each god and goddess and go over the chart with them.

3. Izanagi visits Yomi to find Izanami. Compare his trip to Yomi to Orpheus' visit to Hades. Explain any similarities you find in the two stories. What are the major differences? Also compare and contrast Yomi and Hades.

4. Research the Shinto belief system. Note the major beliefs and practices and find out how many people practice Shinto today. Also, find out how Shinto has changed over the centuries. Organize a report on these topics by using an outline. Then make copies of your outline to hand out to classmates. Ask them to use this outline to jot down notes and questions about each topic as you give your report. At the end of your report, have your classmates ask questions. Try to answer or refer them to a person or book where they might find the answer.

5. Part of Japanese creation myth tells how the wind god destroyed Amaterasu's rice fields. Summarize the story of why the Sun Goddess disappeared. Then show how this myth relates to Japanese culture. Why was rice so important to the early Japanese? What Japanese ceremonies are related to this myth? What symbols of the Imperial family are described in it?

Creative writing activities

1. Write a letter from Izanami to her parents explaining why she and Izanagi left heaven. Then write her parents' response to Izanami's letter. Make your letter as true to the story as possible.

2. Izanagi puts the leech child in a boat and sets the boat adrift. What do you suppose happens to the child after that? Write a story about the events in the leech child's life.

continued

RETOLD WORLD MYTHS
© 1993 Perfection Learning Corporation, Logan, Iowa 51546

3. Choose a Shinto god of nature—a deity of wind, fire, rain, waterfalls, or another. Then write a story about an adventure in the god's or goddess' life.

4. Write a poem about the Shinto view of creation as given in the myth. Focus your poem on the creation of heaven and earth, the Japanese islands, or humans.

5. Why did Izanagi wait so long before he went to rescue Izanami? Suppose he kept a diary and wrote his reasons in it. Write one or two diary entries in which Izanagi explains why he waited so long.

Artistic activities

1. Create a mural of the separation of heaven and earth. Include the rainbow bridge; a view of earth (the Japanese islands, especially); and a view of heaven, the home of the gods.

2. Make a model of Izanami and Izanagi's palace. Include the jeweled spear used as a central pillar. Make your model with cardboard, paper, or other easy-to-find materials.

3. In comic-strip style, draw several "frames" on a strip of posterboard that show one of the children becoming an island. Or show Amaterasu becoming the sun.

4. Construct a model of Izanagi's black headdress. First, ask your librarian to help you find pictures of ancient Japanese headdresses. Use this as a guide when you make the model.

5. Draw or paint a picture of Izanagi's escape from Yomi. You might try doing this as a Japanese scroll painting.

Small-group activities

1. With your group, think of ideas for a card game or board game called "Escape from Yomi." Decide on one or two of the best ideas and test each idea, using "rough drafts" of each game. Then pick one game to fully develop. Write rules and make up game pieces. Have groups of classmates play your game for fun or in a tournament.

2. Read about some Japanese ceremonies or traditions—for birth, marriage, or death. Have group members practice roles in the ritual. You might even come up with costumes for the rite. Then enact the ritual for the class. Have a narrator explain each part of the scene.

Name_____

SPOTLIGHT ON VOCABULARY

Study the words and meanings shown in the box.
Then complete each sentence below by writing the
correct word on the line.

apprehensive—nervous; troubled	**elated**—delighted; overjoyed
banish—cast out	**fidelity**—loyalty; faithfulness
canopy—covering	**humiliation**—shame; dishonor
conduct—manage; direct	**oath**—pledge; promise
cringing—fearful; weak-hearted	**unwittingly**—unknowingly; without meaning to

1. The campers couldn't see the sun because the low clouds formed

   a(n) _____ over the treetops.

2. Fans were _____ when they heard that two free concerts

   would be given.

3. Before taking office, the president-elect must swear a(n) _____ to

   protect the Constitution.

4. Mrs. Kraft thought she had us stumped, but the question was easy.

   She _____ gave away the answer.

5. The proud man chose to walk rather than face the _____ of

   having to beg for a ride.

6. If the government decides to _____ the man, what

   country will he go to?

7. Quang became _____ when his friend's plane was six

   hours late.

8. When Lena and Joseph married, each expected truthfulness

   and _____ from the other.

9. The chairperson called in sick, so who will _____ the meeting?

10. The frightened, _____ animal waited for the bobcat to attack.

Name_____

SETTING THE STAGE

These questions will help you get ready to read
"Rama and Sita." Prepare to discuss the questions
by jotting down answers on the lines.

1. In this myth, the main character gets himself into trouble. Rama is
    overconfident and does not take his enemies seriously.
        On the chart, give two examples of when it is good to have
    confidence. Then give two examples of when too much confidence
    can be dangerous.

Times When Confidence Is Good	Times When Too Much Confidence Is Dangerous
a.	a.
b.	b.

2. Rama believes it is most important to obey his father's wishes. He
    even puts off his own dream to honor his father's promise.

    a. How important do you think is it to obey your parents or other
    adults? Why?

    _____

    _____

    _____

continued

b. When would it be acceptable to stand up for your own ideas,
even if it meant going against your parents? Or would it never be
acceptable? Give reasons for your opinion.

_____

_____

_____

_____

Name_____

RAMA AND SITA

IT HAPPENED LIKE THIS

Write the letter of the best answer on the line.

_____ 1. After Rama's father dies, Bharata wants Rama to
   a. stay away until Kaikeyi calms down.
   b. return home to rule the kingdom.
   c. pray to the gods for his father's soul.

_____ 2. Rama refuses Bharata's request because
   a. of Dasa-ratha's oath.
   b. he thinks Bharata is joking.
   c. Rama now hates his father.

_____ 3. Bharata asks for Rama's sandals because
   a. going barefoot will show Rama's grief.
   b. he has magic boots for Rama.
   c. the sandals will rule until Rama returns.

_____ 4. A wise old hermit gives Rama
   a. the bow of Vishnu and arrows made by the gods.
   b. advice about how to handle Kaikeyi's greed.
   c. the key to a hidden fortress.

_____ 5. Surpa-Nakha is insulted when
   a. Sita refuses to bow to her.
   b. Lakshmana calls Ravana a bad leader.
   c. Rama refuses her offer of marriage.

_____ 6. Lakshmana cuts Surpa-Nakha because she
   a. hisses a curse at Rama.
   b. threatens Sita.
   c. tries to stab him.

_____ 7. The Rakshas are hard to fight because they
   a. are ten times stronger than humans.
   b. seem to appear out of thin air.
   c. can hide in the shadows.

_____ 8. To capture Sita, Ravana does all of the following *except*
   a. make Hanuman call to Lakshmana for help.
   b. send a jeweled deer to lure Rama away.
   c. trick Sita into believing he is a wise hermit.

_____ 9. Hanuman helps rescue Sita by
   a. finding her in Ravana's palace.
   b. sending his monkeys to overpower Vibhishana.
   c. capturing Ravana in battle.

_____ 10. Sita stands in the fire to
   a. earn forgiveness from Lakshmana.
   b. convince Rama to kill all the Rakshas.
   c. prove her fidelity to Rama.

Name_____

VOCABULARY REVIEW

These sentences are taken from the story. Circle
the answer that comes closest in meaning to each
word in **dark type.**

1. " 'Didn't he promise to make you king?' [asked Lakshmana]. 'And didn't
   Kaikeyi make him **banish** his favorite son to the jungle?' "

           a. cast out   b. lead away   c. give up

2. " 'Bharata, you know I can't go back,' [said Rama.] 'My father's **oath**
   holds true—even in death.' "

           a. order   b. magic   c. pledge

3. "Surpa-Nakha laughed at Sita's fear. She turned again to Rama and
   shouted, 'Do you prefer this **cringing** human woman to me?' "

           a. weak-hearted   b. strong-willed   c. white-faced

4. "Rama now saw the danger he had **unwittingly** caused. He swiftly
   leapt between the two women."

           a. suddenly   b. unknowingly   c. boldly

5. "The **canopy** of trees seemed to close overhead, making the jungle even
   darker than usual."

           a. circle   b. clutter   c. covering

6. "Raksha warriors had heard of their princess' pain and **humiliation.**"

           a. unrest   b. shame   c. disease

7. "Finally Rama felt **apprehensive** about being away from his companions
   so long."

           a. nervous   b. unusual   c. insulted

8. "Hanuman agreed immediately to **conduct** the search for Sita."

           a. direct   b. widen   c. announce

9. "Rama was **elated** at the sight of Sita's jewel."

           a. blinded   b. overjoyed   c. silenced

10. "You see, Rama knew in his heart that Sita had been faithful to
    him. But he also knew that others would always doubt her
    fidelity if she were not tested."

            a. loyalty   b. importance   c. wisdom

RETOLD WORLD MYTHS
© 1993 *perfection Learning Corporation, Logan, Iowa 51546*

Name_____

LITERARY FOCUS: THE HEROIC QUEST

Rama's adventures follow a pattern found in many myths. The hero goes on a quest, or a search. During the quest, the hero

- leaves home.
- enters a strange new world.
- completes a task.
- receives a gift.
- returns to share the gift.

The hero's adventures encourage us to look for answers to our questions. They show us ways of coping with our own struggles.

___

These questions will help you see why Rama's adventures are a heroic quest.

RAMA'S HEROIC QUEST

Leaves home	
Why does he leave?	How does he feel?

Enters a new world	
What is the jungle like?	What does he learn there?

Completes a task	
What must Rama do after Sita is abducted?	How does he pass this test?

Receives a gift	
What is Rama's first gift?	What does Hanuman give Rama?

Returns home	
How is he welcomed?	How will he help his people?

continued

Rama is not the only hero who completes a quest. In fact, everyone who becomes an adult must meet the same challenges Rama did.

Complete the chart below. First, think of an experience you and your friends might have. This experience doesn't have to be as spectacular as Rama's. For example, Rama's new world was a dangerous jungle. Most of us are more likely to move to a new school or get a new job. But, like Rama, we must show courage to succeed in our new world. Next, think of some advice that will help you handle this experience well. The first example is done for you.

RAMA'S EXPERIENCE	EXPERIENCE YOU MIGHT HAVE	HELPFUL RULE OR ADVICE
Leaves home		
Accepts banishment	*Moving to a new town or spending some time away from your family*	*Accept the need to move on; be ready to learn from new experiences*
Enters a new world		
Completes a task		
Receives a gift		
Returns home		

Discuss your responses with your classmates.

RETOLD WORLD MYTHS
© 1993 Perfection Learning Corporation, Logan, Iowa 51546

RAMA AND SITA

THE READING-WRITING CONNECTION: UNLOCKING PASSAGES

Answer the questions about these passages taken from "Rama and Sita." (Go back to the story if you need more clues.) Write your response to part *c* of each question on a separate sheet of paper.

1. " 'My father's oath holds true—even in death,' [said Rama]." (page 83)

   a. What does the passage mean as used in the story?

   _____

   _____

   b. Do you think Rama would obey all of his father's wishes—no matter how dangerous or silly? Why do you think the way you do?

   _____

   _____

   _____

   _____

   c. **Journal writing:** Make a list of the five people you feel most loyal to. Then place a number by each person's name to show how loyal you are. Place a *1* by the person's name to whom you are most loyal. Put a *5* by the name of the person to whom you do not have such strong loyalty. For your number *1* person, explain why you feel so loyal.

2. "Rama now saw the danger he had unwittingly caused. He swiftly leapt between [Surpa-Nakha and Sita]." (page 87)

   a. What does the passage mean as used in the story?

   _____

   _____

continued

b. How might Rama have avoided this danger?

_____

_____

_____

_____

c. **Journal writing:** Describe a time when you or someone you
know got into a bad situation by acting foolishly. Tell how you or
the other person handled the situation. What did you learn from the
experience?

3. "But [Rama] also knew that others would always doubt [Sita's]
   fidelity if she were not tested." (page 99)

   a. What does the passage mean as used in the story?

   _____

   _____

   b. Should Rama have allowed Sita to be tested by fire? Explain
   your opinion.

   _____

   _____

   _____

   _____

   c. **Journal writing:** When is it important to prove yourself to
   others? When is it not important to prove yourself? Explain your
   opinions.

RAMA AND SITA

WRITING CORNER: MORAL MYTH

The myth of Rama and Sita teaches several lessons. Indeed, the myth was meant to teach lessons, or morals, to listeners. For example, the myth teaches how to be a good son. Rama obeys his father and honors his wishes. The myth also teaches how to be a good citizen—obey your country's laws, be loyal to your friends, and fight your enemies.

Some of these morals are stated by the characters and narrator. Others are shown by the way the characters act.

Make up your own tale that teaches morals. The following steps will guide you through the process.

1. **The Morals**
   Write three lessons you want your story to teach.

   _____

   _____

   _____

2. **The Story Line**
   Check one of the general plans for your story:

   _____ a character's actions show others how to act

   _____ a character must learn the lessons through trouble or hardships

   _____ a great person teaches the main character the lessons

   _____ your own plan: _____

3. **The Characters**
   Describe the main character, as well as the character's appearance and personality.

   _____

   _____

   _____

   Describe the other character or characters who will be important in the story.

   _____

   _____

   _____

continued

4. **The Setting**
   Describe where and when the story will take place.

   _____

   _____

   _____

5. **The Main Events**
   Briefly describe the major action of the story. (You might try
   simply listing the three or four major events in the plot.) Be sure
   you stick to your story line and tell how the character learns the
   lessons.

   _____

   _____

   _____

   _____

6. **The Story**
   On a separate sheet of paper, write a draft of your story. Use the
   story line, characters, setting, and events you have decided on.
   Then share your draft with a classmate to get suggestions to make
   your story better. You might read it aloud—because sometimes it is
   easier to hear where changes are needed. Finally, rewrite your
   story.

RETOLD WORLD MYTHS
© 1993 Perfection Learning Corporation, Logan, Iowa 51546

RAMA
AND SITA

ONE STEP FURTHER

Class discussion

1. In what ways is Rama a model son? Do you think the Indian idea of a model child is realistic? Why or why not?

2. This myth teaches several lessons about loyalty. Why are Rama, Lakshmana, Bharata, and Sita models of loyalty? How would you define loyalty?

3. Two characters have a conflict of loyalties. What does Kumbha-karna do when he disagrees with Ravana? Contrast Kumbha-karna's response to Vibhishana's. Would you call Vibhishana a traitor? Explain your opinion.

4. Rama's meeting with Surpa-Nakha ends violently. Could conflict with the Rakshas have been avoided? Who was most responsible for the war—Rama, Surpa-Nakha, or Ravana? Do you think that there will be peace in the kingdom while Rama rules? Give reasons for your answers.

5. Describe Sita. In what ways is she a model wife? Why do you think Sita allows herself to be tested by fire? Rama's adventures are a typical heroic quest. Is Sita too a hero? Explain your response.

6. Both Rama and Sita meet and overcome evil. What do they learn about evil? What does this myth teach about how to fight evil?

Oral or written reports

1. This myth takes place in a jungle setting. Read more about the jungles of India. What do they look like? What areas do they cover? What plants and animals are found there? What is the weather like? Do people live in these jungles? If so, how do they live? After you find this information, write a report on what a person might see, hear, or experience if he or she traveled through an Indian jungle.

2. "Rama and Sita" is part of Hindu mythology. Research what Hinduism is. What are the major beliefs? Describe the major gods. How is the religion practiced? Where are Hindus found throughout the world? Report on Hinduism to your class.

3. In many stories, forests and jungles are mysterious places. There people might meet up with magical or evil creatures or have their lives changed forever—for better or for worse. Read two other stories that use forest or jungle settings. Then compare what happens in the jungle or forest to what happens in the jungle in "Rama and Sita." Some possible stories:

  • "The Interlopers" by Saki
  • fairy tales such as "Hansel and Gretel," "Snow White," and "Little Red Riding Hood"
  • selections from *The Jungle Book* by Rudyard Kipling
  • "Finn MacCool's Revenge," an Irish myth
  • "Young Goodman Brown" by Nathaniel Hawthorne
  • "The Most Dangerous Game" by Richard Connell

4. The story of Rama and Sita was first written in the Ramayana. Find out more about this great Indian epic. Why is the god Vishnu considered its hero? What happened after Rama became king? Did Rama ever die? What importance does this epic have today?

5. Find out more about the history of Lanka. Why has its name changed over the centuries? Who has ruled Sri Lanka in the past and who rules it today? What is the island like? What do people do for a living? Why might the ancient Indians have thought it was a place where magical creatures lived? Prepare a report to the class on this country. You might include a map in your report to show where this island nation lies.

Creative writing activities

1. The first time Rama and Lakshmana fought the Rakshas, time seemed to flow "strangely."

continued

The brothers couldn't tell if they had been fighting days or weeks. Write your own short tale in which time flows "strangely" or a character goes backward or forward in time.

2. Write a poem about the rare beauty and magical powers of the jeweled deer.

3. Give an account of what Rama's shoes might say about occupying the throne. You might want to try this as an interview or a comic strip.

4. Suppose Surpa-Nakha had been able to laugh at Rama's teasing. Rewrite the ending of the myth given this change of events.

5. Write a letter from Rama to Sita after she proves her fidelity. Write words of praise for her strength and loyalty or whatever else Rama might have on his mind.

Artistic activities

1. Construct several models of Rakshas in their different shapes and forms. Then hang them from the ceiling or place them "lurking" in your classroom.

2. Draw some political cartoons that show how people felt about Rama not returning to his throne at Bharata's urging. Draw one or two cartoons to show views of people who want him to return. Then draw one or two more cartoons in favor of Rama's staying in the jungle. You might want to look at political cartoons in newspapers and magazines before drawing your own.

3. Create a collage of some important objects in this myth. Include the sandals, the jeweled antlers, Sita's bracelets and necklaces, and Rama's bow and quiver of arrows. You might use materials like construction paper, silver and gold wrapping paper, or marbled paper for your collage.

4. Make a poster of Ravana carrying Sita away in the chariot. Or make one of the sword fight between Rama and Ravana.

5. Prepare a chart or poster showing the guidelines for being a model child, parent, or husband or wife. Take your ideas from the myth. Use fancy lettering—calligraphy—if possible. To finish your project, add a border or other decorations.

Small-group activities

1. Have each group member read a different myth from the Ramayana. Your librarian can help you find these myths. Then practice telling these myths to each other. Try to express mood and emotions in your voice. Then have each group member write a short introduction to another group member's myth. Each person should practice saying his or her introduction. Finally, present the myths to your class or to an outside group.

2. Act out a conversation between Rama and his shoes. You might have Rama tell the shoes about his adventures. The shoes could give Rama news about his kingdom. Other members of your group might play people who give advice to the shoes.

Name_____

SPOTLIGHT ON VOCABULARY

Study the words and meanings shown in the box.
Then complete each sentence below by writing the
correct word on the line.

---

ascended—moved upwards
clusters—groups; flocks
destination—goal; journey's end
diversity—variety
inconstant—changeable; not
    dependable
routine—habit; regular actions

shimmered—glowed; shone
spontaneity—tendency to act on
    impulse or spur of the moment;
    spirit
stable—steady; worthy of trust
suitor—admirer; one who romances
    another

---

1. The _____ of bees formed a great, black, buzzing cloud.

2. Rene's usual _____ after school was to go home, eat an apple, and then practice her trumpet.

3. Alonzo enjoys a _____ of food—Chinese, Italian, and Mexican.

4. Maria rejected one _____ after another because she did not plan to marry soon.

5. The moonlight _____ on the surface of the pond.

6. _____ Liam has always been there when I needed him.

7. At noon the sun has _____ to its highest point of the day.

8. Mickey is a free spirit, known for his _____ and enthusiasm.

9. We hope to arrive in Orlando, our _____ , in two days.

10. I've learned not to count on Serge's being on time because he's as _____ as the wind.

LINDU'S VEIL
OF STARS

SETTING THE STAGE

These questions will help you get ready to read
"Lindu's Veil of Stars." Prepare to discuss the
questions by jotting down answers on the lines.

1. This myth contrasts characters who have routine, predictable lives
    with characters who have few habits or routines. Many people have
    some routines and some unpredictable moments. On the chart, list
    some of your routines. Then write some things you like to do on a
    moment's notice.

Routines	Spur-of-the-moment activities

Now answer this question. Do you think it is better to have a
life that is mainly routine, mostly without routine, or balanced—
with some routines and some unpredictable times? Explain your
opinion to a classmate.

continued

RETOLD WORLD MYTHS
© 1993 Perfection Learning Corporation, Logan, Iowa 51546

2. The main character of the myth, Lindu, is a goddess from a cold northern land. In this land, winter days are very short and summer days extremely long. The far North has spectacular sunsets and moonsets, as well as an electrical show called the northern lights. Also, all the birds must fly south for the winter or die. During the time of the myth, the people still lived in tribes.

   What character traits might a goddess from a land such as this have? Write your ideas on the lines provided below.

Personality:_____

_____

Appearance: _____

_____

Special abilities: _____

_____

Duties or jobs: _____

_____

Name_____

IT HAPPENED LIKE THIS

Write the letter of the best answer on the line.

_____ 1. Lindu's job is to
   a. make the sky ready for the Sun each day.
   b. keep the North Wind from bringing winter too soon.
   c. help the birds plan their winter journeys.

_____ 2. Ukko tells Lindu's suitors that she
   a. is too young to marry.
   b. must make up her own mind.
   c. plans never to marry.

_____ 3. Lindu refuses Sun, Moon, and Pole Star because
   a. Ukko has promised her a gift if she refuses.
   b. they are too routine and boring.
   c. she doubts each one's love for her.

_____ 4. Dazzled by the Northern Lights, Lindu
   a. falls in love and agrees to marry him.
   b. forgets the birds' warnings about him.
   c. plans to run away with him.

_____ 5. Ukko responds to Lindu's engagement by
   a. wishing her happiness.
   b. refusing to speak to her.
   c. asking if Northern Lights is dependable.

_____ 6. The gods and goddesses
   a. make Lindu's wedding dress and veil.
   b. plan a practical joke at her wedding.
   c. plot to keep Northern Lights away from Lindu.

_____ 7. After five nights, Lindu realizes the Northern Lights
   a. never really loved her anyway.
   b. is too undependable to be a good mate.
   c. thinks she's dull and boring.

_____ 8. Since their queen is so upset, the birds promise not to
   a. speak the Northern Lights' name ever again.
   b. sing until the Northern Lights says he's sorry.
   c. fly south and leave Lindu all alone.

_____ 9. Lindu agrees to live in the heavens because there
   a. Ukko can keep the Northern Lights away.
   b. she will be honored.
   c. she can watch over her birds.

_____ 10. As Lindu ascends to heaven, the threads of her veil
   a. get caught between heaven and earth.
   b. turn into a million stars in the Milky Way.
   c. hide the Northern Lights.

RETOLD WORLD MYTHS
© 1993 Perfection Learning Corporation, Logan, Iowa 51546

VOCABULARY REVIEW

These sentences are taken from the story. Circle
the answer that comes closest in meaning to each
word in **dark type.**

1. "Lindu walked along the shore of the sea until she reached the
   clusters of birds."

   a. handfuls   b. flocks   c. lines

2. "[Lindu] wore a simple gown and sandals, but her shawl
   shimmered in the light."

   a. shone   b. melted   c. shrank

3. "Lindu listened carefully to the leaders' reports. Then she told
   some of [the birds] to change their routes. She advised others to
   change their **destination.**"

   a. style   b. map   c. goal

4. " 'Every day you rise, cross the heavens, and set again. Why can't
   you change your **routine** from time to time?' "

   a. news   b. mind   c. habit

5. " 'It's still the same old path day after day,' Lindu answered. 'It
   may seem exciting to you, but I'm used to more **diversity.**' "

   a. understanding   b. variety   c. culture

6. " 'Still, your life lacks **spontaneity,**' Lindu answered. 'Those
   small changes may seem exciting to you, but every day is
   different for me.' "

   a. spirit   b. direction   c. meaning

7. "The next **suitor** for Lindu's hand was not like the others at all."

   a. admirer   b. inspector   c. defender

8. " 'That Northern Lights just isn't dependable,' one of the gods
   said. 'You should have chosen someone more **stable.**' "

   a. gutsy   b. quiet   c. steady

9. " 'He's **inconstant,**' a goddess murmured. 'He never appears
   when you want him to, even if he promised.' "

   a. foolish   b. unsettled   c. slow

10. "Ukko commanded the wind to bring his daughter to him, and
    Lindu **ascended** into the heavens."

    a. appeared   b. rose   c. departed

LINDU'S VEIL OF STARS

LITERARY FOCUS: THEMES

Classic stories—stories that people return to time and again—all contain lasting truths. These truths are often the story's main ideas, or themes. Usually, themes are not stated. Instead, they are shown by words, actions, or events in the story.

Two main themes from "Lindu's Veil of Stars" are given below. First read each theme and example. Then find two other places in the story that show each theme.

---

1. Theme: A person must be dependable to be a good mate.

   a. *"The next night, Lindu and the birds and the gods and goddesses again gathered in the clearing. And again the Northern Lights did not show up. This time, Lindu grew even sadder. . . ."* (page 113)

   b. _____

   _____

   _____

   c._____

   _____

   _____

2. Theme: Variety can make life more exciting.

   a. *Lindu tells the Sun, " 'I couldn't be happy with you. You're just too predictable.' "* (page 109)

   b. _____

   _____

   _____

   c._____

   _____

   _____

continued

RETOLD WORLD MYTHS
© 1993 Perfection Learning Corporation, Logan, Iowa 51546

The following passages feature more themes from "Lindu's Veil of
Stars." These are minor themes, which are not as important in the
story. But, like spices in food, they add richness to a tale. After you
read each passage, write the theme suggested by the passage.

3. Passage: "Many a handsome god spoke to Lindu's father, Ukko,
   King of the Heavens. Each one wanted Lindu for his wife. But
   Ukko said that Lindu must make her own choice of a husband."
   (page 108)

   Theme: _____

   _____

4. Passage: " 'I shall miss you, my feathered friends,' [Lindu] said to
   [the birds]. 'But it is better for you if you start your journeys
   soon.' " (page 108)

   Theme: _____

   _____

5. Passage: "From time to time, Lindu sees the dancing colors of the
   Northern Lights. But from her place in the heavens, she doesn't
   find him as charming as before. And she now understands that he
   is truly undependable. . . .
      'What did I ever see in him?' Lindu wonders." (page 115)

   Theme: _____

   _____

LINDU'S VEIL
OF STARS

THE READING-WRITING CONNECTION:
UNLOCKING PASSAGES

Answer the questions about these passages taken from "Lindu's Veil of Stars." (Go back to the story if you need more clues.) Write your response to part *c* of each question on a separate sheet of paper.

1. "Ukko was happy that his daughter had at last found someone she loved. But he was a little worried about her choice." (page 112)

   a. What does the passage mean as used in the story?

   _____

   _____

   b. Based on what you know about Ukko, tell whether or not you think he is a good parent. Give a reason for your opinion.

   _____

   _____

   _____

   _____

   c. **Journal writing:** Give some examples of times when a parent should worry about his or her child. When do you think a parent worries too much?

2. " 'He was the only one exciting enough for me to love,' [Lindu] wept." (page 113)

   a. What does the passage mean as used in the story?

   _____

   _____

continued

RETOLD WORLD MYTHS
© 1993 Perfection Learning Corporation, Logan, Iowa 51546

b. Do you think that Lindu is right to believe that the Northern Lights is the only one exciting enough for her? Why or why not?

_____

_____

_____

_____

c. **Journal writing:** Lindu has a very definite idea of what she wants in a mate. Describe your idea of a perfect mate or friend. What qualities are most important to you? Which might be most difficult to find?

3. "Ukko . . . knew it would be useless to try to force the Northern Lights to marry Lindu. . . .

"Ukko also knew that those birds who refused to leave their grieving queen would certainly die. So Ukko decided on a different solution to the problem." (page 114)

a. What does the passage mean as used in the story?

_____

_____

b. Give at least two other solutions for this problem.

_____

_____

_____

_____

c. **Journal writing:** Describe a time when you or someone you know had to think of several solutions to a problem before it was finally solved. Which solution worked best? Why?

WRITING CORNER: POINT OF VIEW

This myth is told by a narrator (storyteller) through his or her point of view, or outlook. This point of view affects the way the narrator describes scenes and explains characters' actions.

In this myth, the narrator reveals what most characters are thinking and feeling. Yet after the Northern Lights disappoints Lindu, we never learn what this suitor is thinking or feeling.

Suppose the Northern Lights has just learned that Lindu has gone to heaven. Write a letter from the Northern Lights to Lindu explaining why he did not show up for their wedding. Give his thoughts and emotions. And end the letter as you think the Northern Lights might— either with an apology, a plea, or a good-bye.

1. Put yourself in the Northern Lights' role. Use the organizer below to jot down your ideas for the letter.

Explanation for not showing up for the wedding	Thoughts and emotions now

Conclusion

continued

RETOLD WORLD MYTHS
© 1993 Perfection Learning Corporation, Logan, Iowa 51546

2. Write a draft of your letter on a separate sheet of paper. Then share your work with a classmate and ask for several ideas on how to improve the letter. After you make changes, write your letter in the space given. Be sure to add a closing, such as "Love," "Best wishes," or "With regrets"—whatever fits your letter.

Dear Lindu,

_____

_____

_____

_____

_____

_____

_____

_____

_____

_____

_____

_____

_____

_____

_____

_____

                                        _____
                                        Northern Lights

LINDU'S VEIL OF STARS

ONE STEP FURTHER

Class discussion

1. Why does Lindu fall in love with the Northern Lights? What does she learn from the experience? Does this myth have a happy ending? Give reasons to support your answer.

2. When the Sun romances Lindu, he says that her subjects love her nearly as much as they love him. Likewise, the Moon tells her that she is almost as beautiful as he is. Do you think these suitors are insulting Lindu? Or are they complimenting her? Explain your thinking. If they are insulting her, why do you think she is so polite to them?

3. Although the Northern Lights doesn't keep promises, he is not a totally bad character. What are the good points about him? What are the bad points? If he had been all bad or all good, how might the myth have been different?

4. Lindu believes she and the Northern Lights make a good couple because they are both wild and free. Do you think that people who are alike make a good match? Or do opposites attract? Give reasons for your opinion.

5. Which events or parts of nature are explained by this myth? Which explanations do you like the best? Why? How else could you expand the myth to include other explanations of nature?

Written or oral reports

1. Read more about the aurora borealis, or northern lights. Does the Northern Lights in the myth have any qualities that remind you of the actual northern lights? Why do you think Lindu's favorite suitor is named after the aurora borealis? Report to the class on the northern lights and how they are like or unlike the character in the myth.

2. Find out more about bird migration. You might want to study a specific kind of bird— geese or ducks, for instance. When do they migrate? Why do they migrate, and where do they go? How physically hard is it for the birds to fly long distances? Summarize what you find, and write a short paper on the subject. Include drawings if you wish, or a map to show the migration path.

3. Have the librarian help you find out more about the gods and goddesses of the Finno-Ugric people. Then make a poster to describe these characters and show who is related to whom.

4. Read other myths or tales from Finland, Russia, or Estonia. Ask your librarian to help you find some of these. Then report to your class on the most interesting myths you find.

5. Choose one of these countries to study: Finland, Estonia, Siberia, or Russia. Find out more about the country's art and music. What are some major holidays celebrated? What are the people like? Do they still learn about gods and goddesses of old? Make notes about what you find. Use your data to either prepare a report or a chart that will introduce others to this country.

Creative writing activities

1. Imagine you are Lindu. You know it is going to be hard to find the right suitor. Write an ad that can be used all over your kingdom to help you find a perfect mate. Be sure to write your ad so that suitors will want to respond. Tell what kind of character you are looking for. Describe his personality and physical traits. Also, give suitors some way to contact you (give the message to a bird, whisper to the wind, etc.).

2. Write a poem about a broken promise. You might want to describe the broken promise and include feelings about it. You could write the poem from the point of view of the one who is breaking the promise or the one to whom the promise is broken.

continued

RETOLD WORLD MYTHS
© 1993 Perfection Learning Corporation, Logan, Iowa 51546

3. Suppose Lindu kept a diary. Write four diary entries: (a) after Lindu turns down Pole Star, (b) after she agrees to marry the Northern Lights, (c) after the Northern Lights disappoints her, and (d) after she ascends to heaven and views the Northern Lights again.

4. What if Lindu and the Northern Lights had married? Rewrite the myth beginning with the marriage. Tell what their life together (or apart) is like. Think of a clever ending for the myth.

5. Write your own myth about how the Milky Way was formed, or about why birds migrate.

Artistic activities

1. Make a wedding portrait of Lindu in her veil and gown. As a backdrop, you might use the clearing where the wedding was to take place.

2. Find out about what patterns birds form when they are migrating. Repeat the lines of the formation to make a design or abstract drawing. (Abstract art uses forms and shapes and doesn't try to show a thing as it really is.)

3. Draw a scene where one of Lindu's suitors asks to marry her. Try to capture the suitor's feelings as well as Lindu's.

4. Make a statue of Lindu or Ukko in clay or papier-mâché.

5. Create Lindu's veil using lace and rhinestones or other materials.

Small-group activities

1. Read other myths about romances. These might have either happy or not-so-happy endings. Try to read myths from other cultures—Indian, Native American, Greek, or Norse, for example. Have each group member choose his or her favorite myth. Then have each member make a drawing or painting to illustrate the myth. Finally, review these favorites for the class, using the drawings and paintings during the presentation.

2. In your group, debate whether you think Lindu will ever look for another mate or whether she will stay in heaven forever. Give reasons for your choice. At the end of the debate, vote within the group on the most likely path Lindu's future will take. Then write up a short report on what your group decides. Include arguments for both sides and explain why one choice was more convincing than the other.

Name_____

SPOTLIGHT ON VOCABULARY

Study the words and meanings shown in the box.
Then complete each sentence below by writing the
correct word on the line.

brandished—displayed; waved	**quest**—look; search
forked—split; divided	**sturdy**—solidly built; strong
frantic—wild; out-of-control	**thicket**—thick growth of shrubs or
gratitude—thankfulness;	small trees
appreciation	**transform**—change; alter
prospered—grew well;	**traversing**—traveling over; crossing
increased	

1. We had to decide which way to go when we came to a place where the
   path _____ .

2. The makeup artist managed to _____ the young actress
   into an old woman.

3. The upset man _____ a broom at the mouse to scare it
   away.

4. It was impossible to walk through the _____ with its
   tangled vines and thorny bushes.

5. Claire worked long hours to make sure her new business _____ .

6. The Underground Railroad helped many slaves succeed in their
   _____ for freedom.

7. Heavy rain made the pavement slick, so cars were _____ the
   road slowly.

8. Houses on the coast are built to be _____ enough to stand
   up to hurricanes.

9. As she accepted the trophy, Carline expressed _____ for
   her teammates' support.

10. Tom grew _____ when he saw the band bus leaving
    without him.

Name_____

SETTING THE STAGE

These questions will help you get ready to read "Bao Chu's Search for
the Sun." Prepare to discuss the questions by jotting down answers on
the lines.

In this Chinese myth, Bao Chu goes on a search for the sun. On
the way, he runs into many barriers and problems. Suppose you
described your life as a search. What are you searching for? What
might stop you from reaching your goal?

1. Draw a map or chart of your life. Show your goal. Also show any
    events or successes in your life that will help you reach that goal.
    Include things that might prevent you from reaching your goal as
    well.

    You may choose to show only things that have actually
    happened to you. You might also include things that you expect to
    happen.

continued

2. What kind of person will you need to be to reach your goal? List the traits that will help you succeed.

_____

_____

_____

As you read the myth, notice the traits that help Bao Chu on his search. Are any of the traits similar to those you need to reach your goal?

Phoenix

RETOLD WORLD MYTHS
© 1993 Perfection Learning Corporation, Logan, Iowa 51546

BAO CHU'S SEARCH FOR THE SUN

IT HAPPENED LIKE THIS

Write the letter of the best answer on the line.

_____ 1. Liu Chun promises that if his search for the sun fails, he will
a. become a star to guide others.
b. find another sun.
c. destroy the king of darkness.

_____ 2. Hui Niang wakes from her faint to find
a. the phoenix has left a child in a basket.
b. Liu Chun has sent a boy from the sun.
c. she has given birth to a son.

_____ 3. Bao Chu is an unusual child because he
a. is eighteen feet tall.
b. was born with a sword in his hand.
c. understands what the birds are saying.

_____ 4. Bao Chu takes all of the following on his quest *except*
a. a letter from the wise man.
b. the phoenix.
c. sandals and a coat.

_____ 5. Trapped in the frozen river, Bao Chu is saved by
a. the fiery breath of the phoenix.
b. a warm coat made by the villagers.
c. a beam of light that cuts a hole in the ice.

_____ 6. The phoenix warns Bao Chu about the demon village by
a. dropping Liu Chun's sandal into Bao Chu's cup.
b. attacking the evil king.
c. flying over Liu Chun's grave.

_____ 7. The demon winds torment Hui Niang to make her
a. think Bao Chu will give up his search.
b. cry and break her promise to Bao Chu.
c. believe she made the sun disappear.

_____ 8. Bao Chu and the phoenix find the sun by
a. saying magic words the elders taught them.
b. winning a riddle contest with the demon king.
c. sinking beneath the sea.

_____ 9. At the end of his quest, Bao Chu
a. learns that he will live forever.
b. carries the sun out of the water.
c. brings Liu Chun back to life.

_____ 10. The phoenix continues Bao Chu's mission by
a. lifting the sun into the sky every day.
b. taking care of Hui Niang.
c. guiding others to the sun.

BAO CHU'S SEARCH FOR THE SUN

VOCABULARY REVIEW

These sentences are taken from the story. Circle the answer that comes closest in meaning to each word in **dark type.**

1. " 'Surely the sun will come up again in just a few moments,' said a **sturdy** farmer."

    a. uncommon   b. strong   c. grouchy

2. " 'If I should be killed,' continued Liu Chun, 'I will turn myself into a bright star in the sky. From there I will guide others who **quest** for the sun.' "

    a. search   b. pray   c. wait

3. "Hui Niang looked with **gratitude** at the phoenix, who still stood nearby. [She said,] 'You have kept my son safe for me.' "

    a. thankfulness   b. relief   c. amazement

4. " 'You see, there is your father,' Hui Niang said. 'He told me that he would **transform** himself into a bright star.' "

    a. place   b. shrink   c. change

5. "As Bao Chu came down one mountain, he found himself in the middle of a **thicket** of thorn bushes."

    a. thick growth   b. strong fence   c. ripe harvest

6. "These [thorn bushes] were evil plants that had **prospered** in the land since the sun's disappearance."

    a. fenced in   b. ruled over   c. grown well

7. "After climbing more mountains and crossing more rivers, Bao Chu came to a road that **forked**."

    a. narrowed   b. ended   c. split

8. "While they talked, the phoenix flew in **frantic** circles just above their heads."

    a. swooping   b. wild   c. small

9. "Bao Chu had no difficulty **traversing** the road, even without the phoenix's light."

    a. finding   b. traveling   c. repairing

10. "At that moment, an army of terrible monsters appeared in front of the cave. They all **brandished** sharp weapons and solid shields."

    a. carried   b. prepared   c. waved

RETOLD WORLD MYTHS
© 1993 Perfection Learning Corporation, Logan, Iowa 51546

Name_____

LITERARY FOCUS: FORESHADOWING

Some really amazing events occur in the myth of Bao Chu. A man turns into a star, a coat melts ice, and a demon army disappears. Yet these events aren't a total surprise. That's because these events are foreshadowed.

Foreshadowing is a hint about what happens later in a story. Warnings can be hints. So can physical clues like Liu Chun's slipper. Events, or even a character's mood, can also foreshadow things to come.

The passages below contain foreshadowing. Write the event that is foreshadowed in each passage. The first one is done for you.

1. " 'Where is Liu Chun?' [Hui Niang asked the phoenix.]
   "The phoenix hung its little head as if in sorrow." (page 124)

   What is foreshadowed: *the phoenix has news of Liu Chun's death*

2. " 'If I should be killed,' continued Liu Chun, 'I will turn myself into a bright star in the sky. From there I will guide others who quest for the sun.' " (page 124)

   What is foreshadowed: _____

3. "One day Hui Niang thought she saw a light in the east. But it was not the sun. Instead she saw a bright new star rising into the sky." (page 124)

   What is foreshadowed: _____

4. "Bao Chu . . . turned around and saw a small dark figure approaching him. When the figure came closer, he could see that it was an old woman.
   "Suddenly the phoenix rose up on Bao Chu's shoulder and flapped its wings angrily." (page 130)

   What is foreshadowed: _____

5. "[Bao Chu] thought perhaps he should say good-bye to the old woman more politely. He turned around to speak to her, but she was gone." (page 131)

   What is foreshadowed: _____

continued

Each event below is foreshadowed in this myth. Write the hint that foreshadowed each incident on the lines below. The first one is done for you.

6. Bao Chu dies after he frees the sun.

   Hint: _____ *"Bao Chu would greatly honor his father by completing the quest.*

   _____ *But Hui Niang also knew that she might lose Bao Chu." (page 126)*

7. Bao Chu finds the sun beneath the Eastern Sea.

   Hint: _____

   _____

   _____

8. The demons try to defeat Bao Chu by making Hui Niang cry for him.

   Hint: _____

   _____

   _____

9. Bao Chu needs the bag of soil the villagers gave him to continue his quest.

   Hint: _____

   _____

   _____

10. The army of demons disappears after Bao Chu defeats their king.

   Hint: _____

   _____

   _____

Discuss your responses with your classmates. Also, discuss how a certain mood—like a feeling of fear, or a sense of expectation—sometimes foreshadows coming events. Do any moods in this myth give hints about things to come?

RETOLD WORLD MYTHS
© 1993 **perfection Learning** Corporation, Logan, Iowa 51546

Name_____

THE READING-WRITING CONNECTION: UNLOCKING PASSAGES

Answer the questions about these passages taken from "Bao Chu's Search for the Sun." (Go back to the story if you need more clues.) Write your response to part *c* of each question on a separate sheet of paper.

1. " 'But honored sir, who could hate the sun?' Liu Chun protested gently. . . .

   " 'Think for a moment, young farmer,' said the old man. 'Who benefits from this long night?' " (page 123)

   a. What does the passage mean as used in the story?

   _____

   _____

   b. Why does the elder answer Liu Chun's question with a question?

   _____

   _____

   _____

   _____

   c. **Journal writing:** Can asking questions be the best way to help someone learn? Or does answering a question with a question just confuse people? Give an example to support your view.

2. " 'Don't grieve for me, Mother,' Bao Chu said. 'No matter how long I'm gone, keep up your faith and don't cry. If you shed tears for me, it will break my heart.' " (page 127)

   a. What does the passage mean as used in the story?

   _____

   _____

continued

b. Suppose that Hui Niang had shed tears. Explain how the story would have changed.

_____

_____

_____

_____

c. **Journal writing:** At what times do you welcome sympathy? When would you rather not have sympathy? Explain your feelings.

3. "Luckily, the Hundred Family Coat protected the boy from the freezing ice. The coat's warmth came from more than its fabric." (page 129)

a. What does the passage mean as used in the story?

_____

_____

b. Would Bao Chu's quest have succeeded without the villagers' generous gifts? Explain your opinion.

_____

_____

_____

_____

c. **Journal writing:** Describe a time when someone was kind and generous to you. Then describe a time when you were kind and generous to someone else. Also, tell what emotions you felt.

RETOLD WORLD MYTHS
© 1993 Perfection Learning Corporation, Logan, Iowa 51546

BAO CHU'S SEARCH FOR THE SUN

WRITING CORNER: THE ESSAY

Have you ever said something and then had to prove it? An essay gives you a chance to do just that—on paper. An *essay* is a short piece of writing in which you give an opinion and prove it with details or examples.

"Bao Chu's Search for the Sun" contains several important lessons about life. These are contained in the *thesis* sentences that follow. The thesis is the main idea for your essay. Check the thesis that you wish to write about.

❑ Great wisdom comes with age.

❑ The best gifts are given from the heart.

❑ You can't learn without asking questions.

❑ Working together brings success.

Now organize your essay by completing the outline below.

Thesis sentence:

_____

_____

A. One reason why the thesis is true: _____

_____

   1. Fact or example: _____

_____

   2. Fact or example: _____

_____

B. A second reason why the thesis is true: _____

_____

   1. Fact or example: _____

_____

   2. Fact or example: _____

_____

continued

C. Conclusion (a short summary of your opinion):_____

_____

_____

Now on a separate sheet of paper, write a draft of your essay. Begin with the thesis sentence. Next, use your outline to prove the thesis. At the end of the essay, sum up what you have said. Then read your essay and mark what you want to change. Now write the final version of your essay.

RETOLD WORLD MYTHS
© 1993 Perfection Learning Corporation, Logan, Iowa 51546

ONE STEP FURTHER

Class discussion

1. What makes Bao Chu a hero? Which of his heroic qualities help him most during his search?

2. Bao Chu can't free the sun alone. Discuss how Liu Chun, Hui Niang, the phoenix, and the people of the different villages help him. Why do you think this myth includes so many helpers?

3. In what ways is Bao Chu's mother heroic? Why might Hui Niang be considered an ideal wife and mother?

4. What natural events does this myth explain? Why do you think eclipses were so frightening to ancient peoples?

5. Does Bao Chu completely defeat the evil demons? Is the ending of this myth a happy one? Explain your responses.

Written or oral reports

1. Read other stories about the phoenix in both the Chinese and Greek cultures. What is the most common legend about the phoenix? Also, find out where the word "phoenix" comes from. Where did the Phoenix Islands and Phoenix, Arizona, get their names? Organize your information in a report about the phoenix.

2. What was daily life like in ancient China— in the first and second centuries B.C., for example? Read more about ancient China—its land, culture, and people. Find out something about its government and religion as well. Then give a report on what it was like to live in ancient China.

3. Many Chinese myths are about animals. One animal, the chhi-lin, was a symbol of justice in ancient China. What did the chhi-lin look like? How did the chhi-lin help Kao-yao, a judge famous for his fairness? What did it mean when a chhi-lin was born in a ruler's palace? Share your findings with the class. If possible, show a picture of the chhi-lin.

4. Chinese rulers have tried to destroy their country's myths twice. Research these events by first finding out about the Cultural Revolution. When did it take place? What was its purpose? How did it affect Chinese culture, especially myths and literature? Then compare the Cultural Revolution to Emperor Shih Huang Ti's book burning in 213 B.C. Were Li Szu's reasons for burning books similar to the reasons for the Cultural Revolution? Compare how those who tried to save books and those who resisted the Revolution were punished. How did the book burning affect our knowledge of Chinese myths? Report your findings to the class.

5. Read more about Chinese household gods. Pick two or three of the most interesting gods. Describe these gods to the class and tell what part of the house they ruled. Also, tell some of the most interesting things they did.

Creative writing activities

1. Write your own myth about an eclipse of the sun or about a time when the sun disappeared.

2. Imagine that you are a wise old person. Write what you would advise some of the other villagers to do while they are waiting for Bao Chu to find the sun.

3. The old man tells Liu Chun, " 'Think for a moment, young farmer….Who benefits from this long night?' " Suppose you want to help someone find the answer to a problem—without actually telling the answer. First, invent a problem and write its solution. This could be a tough math problem, a science problem, or even the problem of how to find something that is lost. Then write a list of questions to help guide someone to the solution.

continued

4. Create a story in which you use foreshadowing to make the tale more interesting. Remember, foreshadowing is anything—clues, warnings, events, or moods—that prepares you for later events in a story. Review the myth of Bao Chu to see how foreshadowing is used before you write your own story.

5. What happens to Bao Chu after the myth ends? Is he reincarnated? Does he go to heaven or hell? Read about Chinese beliefs in life after death in the Insights for this myth. Then write what you think might have happened to Bao Chu.

Artistic activities

1. Make a map of Bao Chu's journey. Include the three villages he passes through, the obstacles he faces, the islands he makes, and the cave he finds. You might want to decorate your map with Chinese symbols.

2. Paint a picture of a scene from this myth. You might choose the scene in which the demons try to make Hui Niang cry. Or you might show the sun rising for the first time after Bao Chu's death.

3. Find drawings of the phoenix. Choose the one you like best and make a replica of the bird. Your phoenix might be a model, or you could try to create a Chinese-like painting.

4. Create a smaller version of the Hundred Family Coat.

5. Use clay to make models of the demons and ghosts that turned to stone.

Small-group activities

1. With your group, organize a "mission" for the other classmates to go on—in search of a treasure, to map out a place people rarely visit, or to explore another planet. Plan several obstacles for them to get around. Also, have some members of your group dress up as characters who try to stop you. Before the quest begins, give your classmates some objects that will help them complete the mission.

2. Write a dramatic scene about what happens when the sun returns to Bao Chu's village. Show how the villagers react, what they say about Bao Chu, and how they comfort Hui Niang. Act out your scene for the class.

3. Many Chinese myths were lost because of the book burning described in the Insights. Today many people would like to ban certain books from high school libraries. Others would like to reduce the amount of violence shown on TV. What is the best way to handle controversial books, shows, and songs? Present a debate on this topic. One side might argue in favor of Li Szu's book burning while the other argues against censorship. Ask your classmates to judge which side presents the stronger case. Also ask them which side they agree with and whether the debate changed their opinion.

Name_____

GILGAMESH

SPOTLIGHT ON VOCABULARY

Study the words and meanings shown in the box.
Then complete each sentence below by writing the
correct word on the line.

> **defy**—disobey; challenge
> **destined**—certain; decided
> ___ahead of time
> **fickle**—changeable; uncertain
> **justly**—fairly; with respect
> **menace**—threat; danger
>
> **mock**—make fun of; insult
> **nobles**—upper-class people
> **summit**—top; peak
> **wan**—pale; sickly
> **warily**—with care

1. English lords and ladies are _____ , or members of the
   upper class.

2. When Bing went to give blood, his face turned _____
   and colorless.

3. A _____ person often changes his or her mind from
   one moment to the next.

4. People who _____ the law must often pay a high price.

5. A wise leader rules _____ and honestly.

6. Alberto approached the angry dog _____ and quietly.

7. While crime is always a threat, lack of education might be a bigger
   _____ to society.

8. We planned to climb to the _____ of the mountain
   by the next evening.

9. Because of her musical talent, many believed Kristen
   was _____ to become a great composer.

10. One comedian on TV likes to _____ the president by
    showing him as a little puppet.

Name_____

GILGAMESH

SETTING THE STAGE

These questions will help you get ready to read
"Gilgamesh." Prepare to discuss the questions by
jotting down answers on the lines.

1. At the beginning of this myth, Gilgamesh is not a very good king.
    In fact, he is more like a *tyrant,* or a dictator. But he meets Enkidu,
    who teaches him how to be a good ruler.

    The chart below will help you see the differences between a
    tyrant and a good ruler. For each point given, first write a
    description of a tyrant. Then describe a good ruler. The first one
    has been done for you.

Points of Contrast	Tyrant	Good Ruler
Feelings of those ruled	*hate and fear*	*respect and willingness to obey*
Attitude toward others		
Use of power		
Respect for others' property		
Fairness		

As you read the myth, notice how Gilgamesh changes to become a
better ruler.

continued

RETOLD WORLD MYTHS
© 1993 Perfection Learning Corporation, Logan, Iowa 51546

2. At the end of the myth, both Gilgamesh and Enkidu are beloved heroes. Both are famous for their courage.

   a. Several heroic traits are listed below. Rank them in the order of importance. Use *1* for the most important trait.

   _____ risking danger to help others

   _____ standing up to a bully

   _____ making a big change in your life

   _____ daring to be different

   _____ suffering without complaint

   _____ doing what you know is right despite pressure

   _____ fighting bravely in battle

   _____ showing great physical strength

   _____ facing death

   _____ _____

   b. Explain why the trait that you marked *1* is the most important.

   _____

   _____

   _____

   c. Imagine that a friend is in danger. What are some reasons you might help your friend?

   _____

   _____

   _____

As you read, notice why Enkidu risks danger to help his friend Gilgamesh.

GILGAMESH

IT HAPPENED LIKE THIS

Write the letter of the best answer on the line.

_____ 1. At first, his people fear Gilgamesh because he
    a. takes what he wants from them.
    b. looks as tall as a giant.
    c. threatens them with magic.

_____ 2. Aruru helps the nobles by
    a. creating the wild, strong Enkidu.
    b. warning Gilgamesh never to be cruel.
    c. putting Uruk to sleep until Gilgamesh changes.

_____ 3. Realizing that Enkidu is his equal, Gilgamesh
    a. pretends to be friends with him.
    b. makes friends with him.
    c. plans to fight him again later.

_____ 4. Enkidu teaches Gilgamesh to
    a. never trust a stranger.
    b. believe in himself.
    c. do good and not misuse power.

_____ 5. Gilgamesh challenges Humbaba because
    a. Humbaba plans to attack Uruk.
    b. Gilgamesh will be a hero and Enkidu will seem a villain.
    c. Uruk needs wood and Enkidu needs adventure.

_____ 6. When Gilgamesh pities Humbaba, Enkidu
    a. begs Gilgamesh to show mercy.
    b. rushes over and stabs the monster.
    c. persuades Gilgamesh to kill the monster.

_____ 7. Ishtar lets loose the Bull of Heaven because
    a. she wants to punish the people of Uruk.
    b. Gilgamesh refuses to marry her.
    c. she wants to defy Anu.

_____ 8. Gilgamesh slays the bull and then
    a. boasts that even the gods can't defeat him.
    b. invites all the citizens to a feast of beefsteaks.
    c. takes the bull's tail as a trophy.

_____ 9. Enkidu believes his approaching death is
    a. going to be peaceful.
    b. mostly Gilgamesh's fault.
    c. punishment for mocking the gods.

_____ 10. After Enkidu's death, Gilgamesh always
    a. makes a daily sacrifice to the gods.
    b. remembers his friend and rules fairly.
    c. looks for new adventures.

RETOLD WORLD MYTHS
© 1993 Perfection Learning Corporation, Logan, Iowa 51546

Name_____

GILGAMESH

VOCABULARY REVIEW

These sentences are taken from the story. Circle
the answer that comes closest in meaning to each
word in **dark type.**

1. "But when Gilgamesh came back down into his city, the citizens
   didn't stop to pay their respects. Shopkeepers and **nobles** alike
   hurried to get out of his path."

       a. upper-class   b. wealthy farmers   c. beggars
          people

2. "[The hunter] knew that the king must be informed of this strange
   menace that was running free."

       a. creature   b. god   c. threat

3. "[Enkidu] approached her **warily.** He had never come upon anything
   like this priestess."

       a. silently   b. carefully   c. simply

4. " 'I dreamed of you last night. We were **destined** to meet.' "

       a. wrong   b. certain   c. thrilled

5. " 'The father of the gods has given you great power. But the gods
   intend for you to rule **justly,** not selfishly.' "

       a. pleasantly   b. secretly   c. fairly

6. " 'A challenge is one thing,' replied Enkidu. 'But to openly **defy** the
   gods is another.' "

       a. curse   b. trick   c. disobey

7. "So Gilgamesh helped his friend continue up Cedar Mountain. . . .But
   they knew the monster Humbaba waited for them at the **summit.**"

       a. peak   b. pass   c. cave

8. "[Gilgamesh] knew this **fickle** goddess was dangerous."

       a. threatening   b. quick-tempered   c. changeable

9. " 'I am dying,' [Enkidu] weakly told Gilgamesh. 'I knew it was
   unwise to **mock** the gods. Now they are taking their revenge.' "

       a. insult   b. challenge   c. inflame

10. "But as Gilgamesh looked at his friend's **wan** face, he grew more
    and more worried."

        a. pained   b. restless   c. pale

GILGAMESH

LITERARY FOCUS: FLAT AND ROUND CHARACTERS

In real life, most people have more than one side to them. That is, you will find that serious people can sometimes act silly. Or people you think of as quiet and shy are sometimes loud or angry.

In stories, a character who shows more than one side is called a *round* character. A character who changes in some way is also round, or well-rounded. A character who has only one side—for example, one who is totally innocent or totally evil—is a *flat* character.

Review the traits of each of the following characters. Then decide whether the character is flat (always has the same traits) or whether the character is round (has several different traits). Give three quotes or statements in your own words to support your claim. Note: One piece of evidence is given for Humbaba as an example. You should supply more evidence for item 1.

1. Humbaba is ☑ flat ❏ round

   Evidence: *He is widely feared. He is a terror, with a voice as loud as thunder.*

   _____

   _____

2. Gilgamesh is ❏ flat ❏ round

   Evidence:

   _____

   _____

   _____

3. Ishtar is ❏ flat ❏ round

   Evidence:

   _____

   _____

   _____

continued

RETOLD WORLD MYTHS
© 1993 Perfection Learning Corporation, Logan, Iowa 51546

4. Enkidu is ☐ flat ☐ round

    Evidence:

    _____
    _____
    _____

---

5. Name a flat and a round character from your favorite book, movie, or TV show.

    flat _____

    round _____

6. Round characters are usually more interesting and believable than flat characters. Why, then, do you think writers create flat characters?

    _____
    _____
    _____

Babylonian characters

GILGAMESH

THE READING-WRITING CONNECTION: UNLOCKING PASSAGES

Answer the questions about these passages taken from "Gilgamesh." (Go back to the story if you need more clues.) Write your response to part *c* of each question on a separate sheet of paper.

1. "But try as he might, [Gilgamesh] couldn't move it—the strange stone seemed to fight against him.
     "This immovable object disturbed Gilgamesh." (page 151)

   a. What does the passage mean as used in the story?

   _____

   _____

   b. What do you think the stone represents? Why?

   _____

   _____

   _____

   _____

   c. **Journal writing:** The narrator says that Gilgamesh had never met anything, including the stone, that he couldn't control. Describe something—or someone—that you couldn't control. What were your feelings about not being in control? Can it ever be a good thing not to have total control? Explain your opinion.

2. " 'Father,' the furious goddess [Ishtar] cried, 'Gilgamesh has insulted me! He has accused me of doing terrible things. Worst of all, he has refused to be my husband!' " (page 160)

   a. What does the passage mean as used in the story?

   _____

   _____

continued

RETOLD WORLD MYTHS
© 1993 Perfection Learning Corporation, Logan, Iowa 51546

b. Why does Ishtar become so angry when Gilgamesh refuses her?

_____

_____

_____

_____

c. **Journal writing:** Like Ishtar, people who are upset often look for someone to blame. Describe a time when someone you know blamed another person instead of solving a problem. Also, suggest a better way to handle the situation you describe.

3. " 'Well, that's the end of that!' exclaimed Gilgamesh triumphantly [after killing the Bull of Heaven]. 'Even the gods can't defeat me.' " (page 161)

a. What does the passage mean as used in the story?

_____

_____

b. Does Gilgamesh's boast turn out to be true—that even the gods can't defeat him? Explain.

_____

_____

_____

_____

c. **Journal writing:** List some of the most outrageous boasts or bragging you have ever heard. What were your reactions when you heard these? How do you feel about yourself when you boast? Explain your response.

Name_____   **GILGAMESH**

WRITING CORNER: SETTING

Setting is a very powerful element in a story. Setting isn't just the place or location of a story. The time the story takes place and the overall environment are also part of its setting.

Setting can serve as more than just background information. It may affect characters' actions. For instance, a group of castaways may have to learn how to survive on a desert island. Or it can create a certain mood—with wild winds or gentle breezes, blinding storms or soft rains, fields of flowers or burned landscapes.

1. First, discover more about the setting of "Gilgamesh." Go back to the story to help you answer the questions about setting.

    Historical background
    In what area of the world does the story take place? About what time in history do you think the action occurs?

    _____

    _____

    _____

    Action locations
    The main events in the myth happen in three places: the city of Uruk, the wilderness, and the Cedar Forest. Describe one of these locations.

    _____

    _____

    _____

2. Imagine how the story would change if you changed one part of the setting. For example, what if Enkidu had not grown up in the wilderness? Or what if the Cedar Forest were less dangerous?

    You might change the era in which the story takes place or change just one of the locations. You could also change the characters' lifestyles or beliefs.

    Choose one part of the setting to change. How will you change it? What effect will your changes have on the characters' actions or moods? Write a description two or three paragraphs long that answers these questions and details your changed setting. Share your ideas with the class.

RETOLD WORLD MYTHS
© 1993 Perfection Learning Corporation, Logan, Iowa 51546

GILGAMESH

ONE STEP FURTHER

Class discussion

1. How do the people of Uruk feel about Gilgamesh at first? Describe how their attitude toward Gilgamesh changes. What type of ruler is Gilgamesh at the end of the myth?

2. Why do Enkidu and Gilgamesh become friends? Describe the relationship between the wild man and the king. How does Enkidu fulfill the purpose for which he was created?

3. Give at least two reasons Gilgamesh goes to the Cedar Forest. Why doesn't Enkidu want to go? Why does he accompany Gilgamesh? What part does this trip play in Enkidu's death?

4. Ishtar's father, Anu, doesn't want to release the Bull of Heaven on Uruk. Why do you think the gods keep such a terrible animal? Why does Anu finally let Ishtar have the bull? Was he right or wrong in doing so? Explain your opinion.

5. Gilgamesh has one enemy he can't overcome. How does he feel about his own death? How does he react when Enkidu dies? What is the final outcome of Gilgamesh's search for immortality?

Written or oral reports

1. The epic of Gilgamesh was recorded on clay tablets using cuneiform. Find out more about cuneiform—what it is, which cultures used it. Study the individual forms. Then prepare a poster to show some of these forms and explain their meaning. If possible, include a simple message written in cuneiform on your poster. Be sure to write its translation.

2. Read more about the Sumerian civilization in which the real Gilgamesh lived. Try to imagine what it might have been like to live in this society. If you were a Sumerian citizen, what job or skill might you have? How would you dress? What might your family be like? What would be your daily routine? And who would your friends and associates be? After you find the answers, present a "living history" report to your

class. Pretend to be a Sumerian and tell the class about your life. Let them ask you questions about your life, if you wish. Also, dress the part, if possible.

3. Find out more about Gilgamesh's quest for everlasting life by reading more myths about him. Also, research the Sumerians' beliefs about eternity and afterlife. What did the Sumerians believe would be the perfect eternal life? What did they think happened to a person after death? Do you think the Sumerians feared death? Why or why not? How does Gilgamesh's search for eternal life reflect the Sumerians' beliefs? Report your findings to the class.

4. Read about another legendary person or character. Find some stories about this figure that make him or her seem larger than life.

King Arthur	Queen Guinevere
Cleopatra	Saint George
Odysseus	Annie Oakley
George Washington	Daniel Webster

How do the stories you read compare to the story of Gilgamesh? What traits do Gilgamesh and the figure you chose have in common? In what ways are they different? Tell the class some of the stories you read and explain the differences between the figure you chose and Gilgamesh.

5. The goddess Aruru creates Enkidu from clay. How do people in other cultures believe that humans were first created? Read about the beliefs of people in several cultures. You might choose from India, China, Japan, Egypt, Africa, South America, or your own culture.

Creative writing activities

1. In the myth, the Bull of Heaven is so powerful that it can make buildings topple, just like an earthquake. Write your own myth in

continued

which you explain how earthquakes occur.

2. Suppose Enkidu is able to get a message to Gilgamesh after he dies and reaches the Underworld. What would he say about his life now? Would he have any advice or warnings to give Gilgamesh? Would he have any regrets about dying? Write a note from Enkidu to Gilgamesh.

3. Imagine that some major event in the myth changed:

• Ishtar and Gilgamesh marry
• Enkidu doesn't die
• Gilgamesh becomes proud, angry, and reckless after Enkidu's death

Choose one of the above changes or think of your own. Then rewrite the story from that point. Read your revised myth to the class.

4. The two dreams in this story help foretell and explain future events. Write a story in which dreams play an important role—in predicting the future, explaining the past, or by leading to a fantasy world, for example. Share your story with others.

5. Write a poem to Enkidu and Gilgamesh to be read at the celebration after the warriors killed Humbaba.

Artistic activities

1. Create a replica of some streets and buildings in Uruk. Use clay, cardboard, or other suitable materials. You might want to look at some drawings of ancient buildings of southern Iraq for ideas.

2. Choose your favorite scene from the myth and create a drawing or painting of it.

3. Make a papier-mâché model of what Humbaba or the Bull of Heaven might look like.

4. Put together a costume that a Sumerian might have worn. Use reference books from your library to find out how these ancient people might have dressed.

5. Draw or paint a portrait of Gilgamesh or Enkidu.

Small-group activities

1. With your group, make a mural that includes all of the major scenes in the myth. Decide which scenes to use and what to include in each scene. Make your mural using pastels, markers, or tempera paint. Add bits of material, textures, or other "real" objects, if you wish.

2. Research ancient beliefs in magic. Why did people in earlier times believe in magic? What need(s) did it fulfill for them? What do people today think about ancient beliefs in magic? How does our magic today differ from what the ancients thought of as magic? Have different group members find out the answers to these questions. Then present your information to the class. The following format might be helpful for your presentation:

• Ancient beliefs about magic
• Reasons for the beliefs
• Modern views of the magic of old
• What magic is today (include a few magic tricks, if you wish)

RETOLD WORLD MYTHS
© 1993 Perfection Learning Corporation, Logan, Iowa 51546

RESPONSE KEY

THE DEATH OF OSIRIS
Spotlight on Vocabulary
1. drastic; 2. sorely; 3. former; 4. appease; 5. intrigued; 6. eternity;
7. contended; 8. brooding; 9. intact; 10. fertile.

It Happened Like This
1. a (p. 6); 2. c (pp. 6-7); 3. b (p. 7); 4. c (p. 8); 5. a (p. 9); 6. a (p. 10);
7. b (p. 12); 8. b (p. 13); 9. c (p. 14); 10. a (p. 15).

Vocabulary Review
1. c; 2. b; 3. c; 4. a; 5. a; 6. c; 7. b; 8. b; 9. a; 10. c.

Literary Focus: Characteristics of Myths
1. Osiris is the king who brings life to Egypt and rules the dead. His wife
Iris restores Osiris to life.
2. Characteristics of myths chart
*Note: One example is already given in each category; students need only
supply two more examples, and these will vary.*

Religious beliefs
• A burial place needs to be "pleasant" for a person to enjoy a happy
afterlife.
• Isis prays because she believes the gods will restore Osiris to life.
• Isis also believes in the power of herbs, oils, and potions to restore
Osiris.
• Osiris becomes the ruler of the Underworld.

Values
• The Egyptians valued immortality, as shown by their emphasis on
well-made caskets, intact bodies, and Isis' attempt to make the royal baby
immortal.
• Set is called wicked for trying to destroy Osiris forever and for
bringing suffering to Egypt.
• Osiris is viewed as being good because he rules fairly.
• Isis, Nephthys, and even the creatures of Egypt show compassion.

Explanations of nature
• Egypt's soil mourned at Osiris' death, and the fields were no longer
fertile.
• Once Osiris breathed again, the land came back to life, the fields
turned green, and the trees grew new leaves.

Supernatural elements
• Isis uses her magic to help the handmaidens "with their daily
problems" and to give the royal baby a chance to be immortal.
• The crocodile is able to communicate with Set.
• Isis gives Horus a magic name that will give him power for future
conflicts.
3. *Answers will vary.*

continued

THE TWINS' VISIT TO THE UNDERWORLD

Spotlight on Vocabulary

1. features; 2. felines; 3. ravine; 4. avenge; 5. agile; 6. appetizing;
7. commotion; 8. emerged; 9. soundly; 10. devised.

It Happened Like This

1. a (p. 23); 2. b (p. 25); 3. c (p. 27); 4. b (pp. 27-28); 5. c (p. 30);
6. a (p. 31); 7. a (p. 32); 8. b (p. 33); 9. c (p. 33); 10. c (p. 34).

Vocabulary Review

1. b; 2. c; 3. c; 4. a; 5. b; 6. b; 7. b; 8. a; 9. c; 10. a.

Literary Focus: Conflicts

1. b. Conflict: The twins are sent to the House of Knives where fiends
want to eat them, *or* they must find flowers to give to the Xibalba the
next day.
Solution: The twins convince the fiends they aren't tasty and promise
them animal meat. Later, they get the ants to bring them flowers.
c. Conflict: The cold could freeze the twins to death.
Solution: They find wood and pine knots and build a fire.
d. Conflict: The jaguars threaten to kill and eat the twins.
Solution: The twins find bones to give the jaguars.
e. Conflict: Flames dance around the twins.
Solution: The twins avoid the flames.
f. Conflict: Bats with razor-sharp wings attack the twins, and Hunahpú's
head is severed.
Solution: Ixbalanqué makes a substitute head with the help of a turtle.
This works until Ixbalanqué and the rabbit get Hunahpú's own head back.
g. Conflict: The lords invite the twins to play a game of jumping into a
bonfire. The twins are burned to ashes.
Solution: The twins have gained immortality, so they are resurrected.
They return to Xibalba and trick the lords into jumping into fire. But the
twins don't restore the lords to life.
2. *Answers will vary.*

FINN MACCOOL'S REVENGE

Spotlight on Vocabulary

1. wavered; 2. quarry; 3. integrity; 4. allegiance; 5. hearth; 6. truce;
7. agonized; 8. vaulted; 9. scowl; 10. donned.

It Happened Like This

1. a (p. 44); 2. c (p. 45); 3. c (p. 47); 4. b (p. 48); 5. a (p. 50);
6. a (p. 52); 7. c (p. 53); 8. b (p. 55); 9. a (p. 56); 10. c (p. 57).

Vocabulary Review

1. a; 2. c; 3. c; 4. a; 5. b; 6. b; 7. a; 8. b; 9. b; 10. a.

Literary Focus: Exposition

Responses will vary.

The Times

1. A king, who is also a great warrior, rules the land.
2. Warriors are honored by the king—so they must have a high position.
3. Grainne's engagement is typical because she has been pledged to an
older man and her father has pledged her.

Characters and Situations

4. a. Grainne is bold, willful, and used to getting her own way.

b. She is unhappy about her engagement to Finn MacCool.

c. Since she is bold, she gets to know Diarmuid and convinces him to marry her and help her escape from Finn. She even uses magic on him and others to make sure events go her way.

5. a. Finn MacCool is brave and mighty but wears a permanent scowl. He is an older man.

b. Finn is about to be married to Cormac's daughter, and he is being honored at a banquet. He has the best of everything—the best warriors and the best hounds and horses. He also has the power to heal.

c. Since Finn is older, Grainne doesn't want to marry him. Like Grainne, Finn is also used to having his own way. His position is challenged when Diarmuid takes Grainne. He becomes angry, jealous, and bent on revenge. Years later, he fails to act quickly to save Diarmuid—because of these old feelings.

6. a. Diarmuid is known as one of the greatest fighters. He is young, handsome, brave, and noble. Also he is loyal and has integrity.

b. Others regard him highly. The warriors and Finn can depend on him, and he has sworn loyalty to Finn. At the beginning of the story, he is at a banquet to honor Finn and Grainne. He is seated next to Grainne.

c. Sitting next to Grainne, Diarmuid gets to know her, is charmed by her, and pledges loyalty to her. This leads to his conflict with Finn—after Diarmuid helps Grainne escape and later marries her.

IZANAMI AND IZANAGI

Spotlight on Vocabulary

1. surveyed; 2. revive; 3. pillar; 4. perish; 5. ceremony; 6. molded; 7. presence; 8. searing; 9. pathetic; 10. intruder.

It Happened Like This

1. b (pp. 63-64); 2. a (p. 65); 3. c (p. 66); 4. c (p. 68); 5. b (p. 69); 6. c (p. 71); 7. a (p. 71); 8. b (p. 72); 9. a (p. 73); 10. c (p. 73).

Vocabulary Review

1. c; 2. a; 3. a; 4. b; 5. c; 6. a; 7. c; 8. c; 9. b; 10. c.

Literary Focus: Images

1. *The first example is provided for students.*

Smell: sweet-smelling flowers

2. Touch: searing heat of the god of fire; Izanami's burns and paralyzing fever

3. Touch: feeling of extreme hunger

4. Sight: Izanagi pacing; the beautiful palace and island

Sound: singing waterfalls, streams, and trees

5. Touch: darkness that surrounds; Izanagi feels the path with his foot and senses his wife's presence

6. Sound: Izanami's whisper; a voice that sounds unhappy; a whisper that becomes a long, sad sigh

7. Sight: Izanami's decaying body and rotting flesh falling from her bones; maggots feeding on the body

8. Sound: sound of hissing and scurrying

continued

9. "The waterfalls, streams, and trees all sang to [Izanagi]."

10. The figurative image does more than appeal to the sense of sound. It also includes a metaphor, comparing the sounds of nature to singing.

RAMA AND SITA

Spotlight on Vocabulary
1. canopy; 2. elated; 3. oath; 4. unwittingly; 5. humiliation; 6. banish; 7. apprehensive; 8. fidelity; 9. conduct; 10. cringing.

It Happened Like This
1. b (p. 82); 2. a (p. 83); 3. c (pp. 83-84); 4. a (p. 84); 5. c (p. 86); 6. b (p. 87); 7. b (p. 88); 8. a (pp. 91, 93); 9. a (p. 96); 10. c (p. 100).

Vocabulary Review
1. a; 2. c; 3. a; 4. b; 5. c; 6. b; 7. a; 8. a; 9. b; 10. a.

Literary Focus: The Heroic Quest
Responses will vary.

Leaves home: Rama leaves because of his father's promise to banish him to the jungle for fourteen years. He accepts his exile because he honors and obeys his father.

Enters a new world: The jungle is a wild place with many unknown dangers. Rama learns to take its dangers seriously.

Completes a task: Rama defeats Ravana and rescues Sita. He asks for help from the monkeys and wins a battle against the Rakshas.

Receives a gift: A hermit gives Rama the bow of Vishnu, which he uses to kill Ravana. Hanuman brings news of Sita and guides Rama to Ravana's palace.

Returns home: His people are glad to see Rama and are ready to accept him as their ruler. Rama has already defeated the Rakshas; he will continue to protect his people and set a good example for them.
Answers in the experience chart will vary.

LINDU'S VEIL OF STARS

Spotlight on Vocabulary
1. clusters; 2. routine; 3. diversity; 4. suitor; 5. shimmered; 6. stable; 7. ascended; 8. spontaneity; 9. destination; 10. inconstant.

It Happened Like This
1. c (p. 108); 2. b (p. 108); 3. b (pp. 109-110); 4. a (pp. 111-112); 5. c (p. 112); 6. a (p. 112); 7. b (p. 113); 8. c (p. 114); 9. c (p. 114); 10. b (p. 115).

Vocabulary Review
1. b; 2. a; 3. c; 4. c; 5. b; 6. a; 7. a; 8. c; 9. b; 10. b.

Literary Focus: Themes
Responses will vary. Following are sample responses. Students may quote or paraphrase.

1. a. *This first one is done for students.*

b. " 'That Northern Lights just isn't dependable,' one of the gods said. 'You should have chosen someone more stable.' " (p. 113)

c. "[Lindu] now understands that [the Northern Lights] is truly undependable. Someone like that could never help take care of her birds. He would never be there when needed." (p. 115)

2. a. *This first one is done for students.*

b. " 'Still, your life lacks spontaneity,' Lindu answered. 'Those small changes may seem exciting to you, but every day is different for me. One day I might explore a cave and play in the sand. The next I might watch as my new birds hatch and grow their feathers. . . . I could not be happy with your routine life.' " (p. 110)

c. "So the Moon went on his way and continued his nightly journey across the sky. He was especially large and bright that night. But Lindu wouldn't change her mind." (p. 110)

3. A person should make his or her own decisions in important matters.

4. Sometimes the needs of others are more important than our own.

5. A person's feelings toward another person can change, *or* It's hard to keep loving someone who's undependable.

BAO CHU'S SEARCH FOR THE SUN

Spotlight on Vocabulary

1. forked; 2. transform; 3. brandished; 4. thicket; 5. prospered; 6. quest; 7. traversing; 8. sturdy; 9. gratitude; 10. frantic.

It Happened Like This

1. a (p. 124); 2. c (p. 125); 3. a (p. 125); 4. a (pp. 126-127); 5. b (p. 129); 6. a (p. 132); 7. b (p. 134); 8. c (p. 135); 9. b (pp. 136-137); 10. a (p. 138).

Vocabulary Review

1. b; 2. a; 3. a; 4. c; 5. a; 6. c; 7. c; 8. b; 9. b; 10. c.

Literary Focus: Foreshadowing

1. *This one is done for students.*

2. Liu Chun's quest will fail, *or* after Liu Chun's death, his son will continue his mission.

3. Liu Chun is dead.

4. Bao Chu is in danger.

5. The old woman is not human.

6. *This one is done for students.*

7. The elder tells Liu Chun, " 'There is a demon king who rules over all evil creatures. I believe that he has stolen the sun and hidden it away. He is the only one who could do such a thing. . . . He lives beneath the Eastern Sea.' " (p. 123)

8. "But Hui Niang remembered what Bao Chu had said: 'If you shed tears for me, it will break my heart. With a broken heart, I will weaken and will not be able to complete my father's quest.' " (p. 127 or p. 134)

9. The elder of the second village tells Bao Chu, " 'The most valuable thing we have is our soil. . . . Perhaps it will be useful to you.' " (p. 130) *or* " 'Why don't you leave that bag of dirt here on the side of the road?' " the old [demon] woman suggested [to Bao Chu]. 'It's silly to carry such a useless burden. It must be growing heavy.' " (p. 131)

10. " 'That must be the demon king,' Bao Chu thought. 'If I kill that one, . . . the others will disappear.' " (p. 136)

continued

GILGAMESH

Spotlight on Vocabulary

1. nobles; 2. wan; 3. fickle; 4. defy; 5. justly; 6. warily; 7. menace;
8. summit; 9. destined; 10. mock.

It Happened Like This

1. a (p. 146); 2. a (p. 147); 3. b (p. 152); 4. c (p. 152);
5. c (pp. 153-154); 6. c (p. 158); 7. b (p. 160); 8. a (p. 161);
9. c (p. 161); 10. b (pp. 162-163).

Vocabulary Review

1. a; 2. c; 3. b; 4. b; 5. c; 6. c; 7. a; 8. c; 9. a; 10. c.

Literary Focus: Flat and Round Characters

Evidence will vary.

1. Humbaba is flat. He is a terror, with a voice as loud as thunder. He threatens Gilgamesh and fights to kill. Then when he is down, he tries to trick Gilgamesh into sparing his life. When he dies, the narrator says all evil vanished from Cedar Mountain.

2. Gilgamesh is round. At first, he is reckless, fierce, and angry. He won't listen to his people and intrudes upon them. After Enkidu becomes his friend, Gilgamesh learns to be a fair and wise ruler. He is still daring and bold and even mocks the Bull of Heaven. He grieves deeply when Enkidu dies. Even though he is bitter about the death, Gilgamesh remains a fair king.

3. Ishtar is flat. She is fickle and dangerous. When Gilgamesh turns down her proposal, she unleashes the Bull of Heaven to kill people and wreck Uruk. Then when Gilgamesh insults her, she becomes even more angry and threatening.

4. Enkidu is round. He appears wild and untamed, but he is smart and willing to learn civilized ways from the priestess. When he becomes civilized, he loses some of his animal strength. Later Enkidu teaches Gilgamesh to be good, just, and unselfish. Enkidu expresses sadness (when he misses the wild), fear (of Humbaba), bravery (in fighting Humbaba), and humility (after he and Gilgamesh anger the gods).

5. *Answers will vary.*

6. *Answers will vary.*